Why We Do What We Do

Why We Do What We Do

DR HELENA BOSCHI

LANSONS
Advice Ideas Results

ABOUT THE AUTHOR

Helena Boschi is a psychologist specialising in applied neuroscience. Helena has held senior talent-management positions within international companies and now works across a range of industries worldwide.

Helena's work with her clients, through her company Chequered Leopard, involves designing new and creative learning initiatives, particularly in the areas of leadership and team development, intercultural communication and organisational change.

Helena combines neuroscience with relevant insights and practical application. Her work is dedicated to encouraging people to take greater responsibility for the long-term functioning and health of their brain.

chequered leopard

ACKNOWLEDGEMENTS

As many of my friends and colleagues know, writing this book has been a long-term ambition. I have been promising to provide a resource like this for a number of years but I have never managed to find the right amount of time to commit to putting it together.

And then my work brought me into contact with Suzanne Ellis, a director at Lansons. From the beginning, Suzanne has urged me to write this book and has been an invaluable source of energy and guidance. During the course of our professional engagements – Suzanne's focus on shaping employee communication and change initiatives, and my work in applied neuroscience and executive-development programmes – we have both come to recognise the critical importance of brain health and wellbeing. Through this book our aim is to provide a useful guide for anyone who has an interest in understanding how they can get the best out of their own brain and the brains of those around them.

I am grateful to Lansons, and in particular to Suzanne, for their ongoing help and support in publishing this book. I look forward to working with Lansons in a complementary capacity.

I also owe a great deal to Denise Jagger, a partner at Eversheds Sutherland, who has given my work and this book a great deal of her time and who has always been wonderful to work with.

Thank you to the scientists, authors and psychologists who have permitted me to feature their work, as well as those whom I have cited throughout this book. Without them, it would not exist.

A huge debt of gratitude goes to the many wonderful people who have encouraged me to write this book and who have always shown so much enthusiasm for what I do.

My thanks also go to Dr Steve Trenoweth, who provided me with advice and guidance throughout the whole process. His experience, wisdom and humour are always hugely valued.

Finally, my overwhelming appreciation goes to Stephen, my husband, business partner and best friend. Over the years Stephen has championed me through my PhD, my research and now this book. He has been an unfailing provider of love, encouragement, care and ideas. I really could not have done this without him.

We will be donating 10% of profits, to be shared equally, between Lansons' charity of the year, Mind, to make sure that anyone with a mental health problem gets the support they need, and St Giles Trust, an award-winning charity supported by Eversheds Sutherland that helps ex-offenders, many of whom have mental health problems.

'The aim of science is always to reduce complexity to simplicity.'

William James

Influential philosopher and psychologist (1842–1910)

FOREWORD

Why this book?

How many of us are now living in a world where we
are never off? Technology is everywhere, connecting
and consuming us. It has transformed the way we think,
communicate and even live. We rely on being plugged in
to instant information and real-time feedback. We no longer
have to wait for anything: technology has enabled us to
have it all now. We can shop, read and watch movies and
television programmes whenever we want. We are even
able to choose a potential partner simply by swiping right.
We are increasingly defined by speedy responses and
even faster results. Immediacy is what we all now expect
and demand.

The ramifications of this modern world are both good
and bad. A world without search engines and instant
access to data is unimaginable today: we can automate
tasks, coordinate activity, exchange information, direct
our own education and access others' opinions at the touch
of a button. The downside is that we are subjected to the
whims of a fickle, virtual network that can validate and
endorse, or demean and destroy. Our identity and success
are forged by social opinion and follower numbers, where
relationships are tenuous and often temporary.

Organisations talk increasingly about *innovation* and *trust*
as vital new world commodities and yet many seem to do
everything possible to crush creative and collaborative

effort in their relentless drive for quick results. What we seem to have lost sight of is that we are all essentially social, emotional, sensual and flawed beings, hampered by our own biology and biases. The same *humanness* that has given rise to so much amazing discovery is, at the same time, limited in its ability to cope with the world that we have now fashioned for ourselves.

Put simply, the human brain is designed primarily to keep us alive and functioning, but it has not yet adapted quickly or well enough to deal with the now-constant bombardment of information and accompanying demands. Our instinct to survive means that we are naturally prone to interruption, but we do not have the brainpower to deal with the number of inputs we are now receiving.

So while every advance and latest innovation in technology gives us the illusion of greater efficiency and control over our life, it comes at a cost. Never-ending data overload feeds a desire and an obligation to respond to everything. But in our frenzy to feel productive and seek instant rewards – which, in turn, becomes addictive – we deny ourselves the space and time to slow down, breathe deeply and build long-term, meaningful relationships.

Our brain deals with this continuous loop of uncertainty and anxiety by releasing chemicals to protect us from any potential threat or danger, and to keep us alive. These chemicals place us in a state of alertness, tension and stress that influences our view of the world and distorts our thinking. And we cannot think clearly when we are focused on survival.

Our modern lifestyle is not helping. We are sitting too much and we are exercising and sleeping too little. Because our bodies are not active and mobile, we are witnessing an increase in depression, stress, obesity and degenerative illnesses such as dementia.

And so, as technology frees up effort in one area, we need to work harder to manage the fallout in another. The rapidly changing world around us therefore demands conscious effort and an understanding of our basic biological imperatives.

The good news is that we can all develop strategies and techniques to help us lead happier, healthier and more fulfilling lives. Learning about how our brain functions is an important first step.

Ongoing research in neuroscience provides us with valuable insights into why we do what we do. This book presents some of these insights and offers ideas as to how to apply them to everyday life.

How to read this book

The intention is that this book should strike a balance between knowledge and application by combining scientific research with concrete examples and illustrative stories. It is designed to be visual, practical and easy to read.

Each chapter is written as a stand-alone guide to a particular brain area and concludes with five tips for improving brainpower in that area. Additional references to specific studies are also provided for those who would like to explore these in more depth.

It is important to point out that, although the chapters are organised under separate, recognisable headings, it would be too simplistic to suggest that the brain works in a similarly clear-cut way. There are therefore inevitably some areas of overlap between chapters, which reflect the extensive activity and multifaceted nature of our brain.

As neuroscience continues to gain momentum, more studies will undoubtedly be published. In the meantime, I hope that this book will whet your appetite and leave you wanting to find out more.

Remember: it is always valuable to ask 'why'.

Why do we need to keep our brain in balance?

Why are we emotional rather than rational?

Why do we not remember accurately?

Why can we not multitask?

Why does our brain love (and hate) certain words?

Why do we not see the truth?

Why are we all biased?

Why do we need to reignite our creativity?

Why do most change efforts fail?

Why do we need to manage our stress?

Why do leaders need to learn about the brain?

Why do we need to improve our lifestyle and daily habits?

Chapter overview

Chapter 1 provides a quick look at our brain – how it is structured and how it functions – and it also considers male/female differences and the nature/nurture debate.

Chapter 2 explores our emotional brain; why we have emotions and how our emotions affect our memories.

Chapter 3 looks at how memory works in our brain, the different types of memory we store and how to improve our ability to remember.

Chapter 4 discusses our attentional system, its strengths and limitations, and why focus is essential to learning.

Chapter 5 considers the impact and use of language, the power of certain words and the endurance of storytelling.

Chapter 6 offers insights into visual perception, explaining how our brain 'sees' and why we are susceptible to visual illusions.

Chapter 7 describes some of the biases that we carry within us and discusses why we have developed mental shortcuts to interpret information.

Chapter 8 enters the world of the creative brain and provides some insights into how to reignite the creative spark that we all carry within us.

Chapter 9 discusses the impact of change on our brain, explaining how habits are formed and how we can minimise the pain of change.

Chapter 10 provides information about what stress is doing to us in today's world. It also describes the different symptoms associated with stress, and offers some methods of handling stressful situations.

Chapter 11 looks at leadership and how effective leaders need an understanding of the brain in order to get the best out of the people they lead.

Chapter 12 offers a glimpse into our modern lifestyle and considers how we should protect our brain against daily challenges, with a specific focus on sleep, exercise and food.

'Sitting on our shoulders is the most complicated object in the known universe.'

Michio Kaku

Theoretical physicist and futurist (1947–)

1: OUR BRAIN

The brain is the basis of everything we do: how we behave, feel, remember, pay attention, create, change, influence and ultimately live. Learning about how our brain functions is an important starting point to understanding why we do what we do.

Even though it weighs only three to four pounds, our brain is complicated. Despite new advances in neuroscience, neurobiology and neuropsychology, the brain remains the most mysterious, complex and relatively unknown organ in the human body.

This chapter provides an introductory overview of the main structures and functions of the human brain. It explains how our brain helps us respond to the world around us and keeps our system in balance. Some insights are offered into male/female brain differences, whilst also acknowledging the influences of our environment and upbringing.

As we begin to understand more about how our brain works, we become more aware of our own thoughts, responses, behaviours and emotions. We also become better equipped to get the best out of our brainpower in the future.

Part 1: The science explained

The key function of our brain is to keep us alive. This means that the brain needs to be able to anticipate what is safe or harmful in our environment.

In other words, our brain is our *personal prediction machine*. It is constantly scanning and processing the world around us to help us respond appropriately.

Why we need to keep it all in balance

The brain maintains a finely tuned internal balance in order to regulate our heartbeat, breathing, temperature, water, hormonal release and sugar levels. This internal balance is known as *homeostasis*, meaning 'same state'.

Our internal body environment is kept steady and stable despite changes in our external surroundings. This balancing act works on what is called a *negative-feedback loop*: when the level of something rises, our brain's control systems reduce that level, and when the level of something falls, our brain's control systems raise that level.

For example, if we are cold we shiver, in order to generate heat, and if we become too hot we sweat, in order to cool down.

Our brain works hard to maintain this balance and to keep our system functioning effectively.

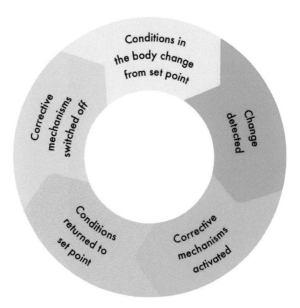

Figure 1.1: The negative-feedback loop

Our brain, neurons and synapses

Our brain represents just 2% of our total body weight and is made up of approximately 100 billion nerve cells, which are known as *neurons*.

Each neuron can make between 1,000 and 10,000 connections, or *synapses*, with other neurons. Our brain's ability to form new connections, constantly reorganising itself and changing its pattern and shape, is known as *neuroplasticity*. We have two different types of neurons – *sensory* and *motor*:

» **Sensory neurons** carry information from our sensory organs – eyes, ears, nose, tongue and skin – to the brain.

» **Motor neurons** carry messages away from the brain and spinal cord to our muscles.

Our brain has three main parts: *forebrain*, *midbrain* and *hindbrain*. The midbrain and hindbrain make up the brain stem and connect the forebrain to the spinal cord. The forebrain contains the *cerebrum*, the largest part of the brain, which plays a critical role in processing information.

Our four lobes . . .

The **cerebrum** is divided into four *lobes*. Although these are all interconnected, each lobe is associated with different functions.

Frontal lobe

Parietal lobe

Occipital lobe

Temporal lobe

Figure 1.2: The lobes of the brain

Frontal lobe   Processes higher cognitive functions and decision-making. This is the centre of our brain's executive functioning and manages complex mental and behavioural responses to the environment.

Temporal lobe   Controls our hearing and processes
memories, integrates them with our senses
and emotions, and regulates our endocrine
system, which releases our hormones.

Parietal lobe   Processes information about temperature,
taste, touch, movement, reading and
spatial orientation.

Occipital lobe   Primarily responsible for vision and the
interpretation of information taken in by
the eyes.

Our lobes work together to enable our brain to operate as a
whole and to adapt constantly to keep us functioning. If we lose a
sense, such as sight, another sense such as hearing gets stronger.
The *seeing* part of the brain is then used to process sound.

. . . and two hemispheres

Most mental functions are distributed across the right and left
sides, or *hemispheres*, of our brain. Certain mental processes
and tasks are specialised to either one hemisphere or the
other. This is known as *lateralisation* of brain function.
Scientists believe that this is our brain's way of being
more efficient: by avoiding duplication we optimise our
available brainpower.

Our knowledge of the brain's hemispheres can be largely
credited to the work of Dr Roger Sperry during the 1960s. Dr
Sperry examined the way our brain's hemispheres operate both
independently and together and, in 1981, was awarded the
Nobel Prize in Physiology or Medicine for his work in this area.

» The **left hemisphere** normally directs logical, analytical, mathematical and verbal tasks.

» The **right hemisphere** is generally more concerned with music, emotion and tonality, facial recognition, visual imagery and abstract information.

The right hemisphere controls the muscles on the left side of our body, while the left hemisphere controls the muscles on the right side. Damage to one side of the brain, such as that caused by a stroke, affects the opposite side of the body.

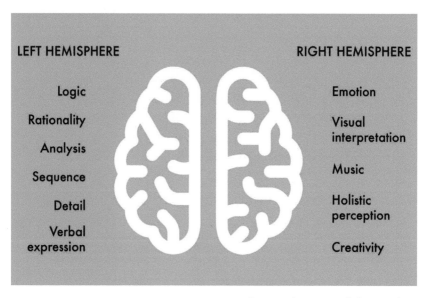

Figure 1.3: Our two hemispheres and their roles

Connecting the two hemispheres is a network of fibres, called the *corpus callosum*, which enables information to be carried between the hemispheres. The primary function of the corpus callosum is to ensure that our brain functions as one integrated and cohesive unit.

How neurons communicate with each other

All of our neurons pass on information to other neurons. In order to do this, our brain communicates on both an electrical as well as a chemical level, involving ions such as sodium, potassium and calcium. Communication between neurons is the core of all our thoughts, emotions and behaviours.

Any new experience stimulates an electrical impulse within a neuron. Electricity cannot travel across a gap or space, called the *synaptic cleft*, so when this impulse reaches the end of the neuron the information has to be relayed by chemicals, known as *neurotransmitters*.

Neurotransmitters are stored in small compartments called *vesicles*. Each vesicle tends to hold one type of neurotransmitter. The neurotransmitters travel in their vesicles to the end of the neuron where they wait to cross over the gap. At the right time, the neurotransmitter is emptied into the gap and travels across to the other neuron. When neurotransmitters travel between neurons, they form a connection with another neuron.

All of this happens with impressive speed and precision.

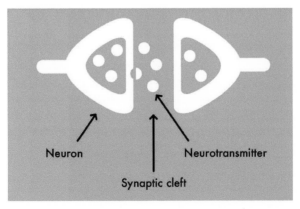

Figure 1.4: Neurons and neurotransmitters

Neurotransmitter		Role	Some symptoms of deficiency
Serotonin	☺	Inhibitory neurotransmitter. Plays an important role in regulating mood, happiness, relaxation, appetite, memory, bowel function, learning and hormonal release.	Depressed mood, anxiety, panic attacks, low energy, sleeping problems, feeling tense and irritable, impaired memory and concentration.
Oxytocin	♡	Also known as the *cuddle chemical* or *moral molecule*. Plays a key role in maternal bonding, childbirth, social affiliation and increases romantic attachment and empathy. Makes us more sensitive to social cues around us.	Anxiety, stress, feelings of disconnect with others, depression, loss of appetite, greater sensitivity to pain. Used to accelerate childbirth and improve social engagement in people with autism.
Dopamine		Both excitatory and inhibitory neurotransmitter. Responsible for movement, memory, pleasurable reward, attention, desire and drive to get things done. Known as our *motivation molecule*. Controls movement and posture.	Memory problems, poor concentration, difficulty initiating or completing tasks, lack of energy, lack of motivation, addictions, cravings, compulsions, a loss of satisfaction and libido. Too little dopamine is implicated in Parkinson's Disease.
Glutamate		Major excitatory neurotransmitter in our brain. Involved in cognition, memory and learning.	Insomnia, problems concentrating, mental exhaustion and depleted energy.
GABA		Inhibitory neurotransmitter. GABA (gamma-amino butyric acid) acts as a natural sedative and tranquilliser and calms nervous activity. Contributes to motor control and vision.	Anxiety disorders, racing thoughts, bipolar disorder, mania, poor impulse control, panic attacks, cold hands and shortness of breath.
Acetylcholine		Widely distributed excitatory neurotransmitter. Major impact on wakefulness, attentiveness and arousal. Needed to turn short-term memories into long-term ones. Released to activate muscles. (Botox is a neurotoxin that blocks the effect of acetylcholine, preventing the facial muscles from moving.)	Low energy levels, memory loss, learning problems, muscle aches, cognitive decline. People with Alzheimer's Disease have altered levels of acetylcholine. Also implicated in Parkinson's Disease.
Noradrenaline		Excitatory neurotransmitter. Triggers changes in the body in response to stress (increased oxygen, heart rate and glucose) to raise our alertness and *fight or flight* capacity. Important for attentiveness, emotions, dreaming and learning.	Depression, loss of alertness, memory problems, lack of energy, focus and motivation.

Figure 1.5: Neurotransmitters and their roles

Neurotransmitters affect our mood, memory and wellbeing. They are effectively our *chemicals of emotion.*

There are two types of neurotransmitters: *excitatory* and *inhibitory.*

» **Excitatory neurotransmitters** stimulate the brain.

» **Inhibitory neurotransmitters** calm the brain and balance brain stimulation.

The impact of neurotransmitters on our health is the focus of ongoing scientific research. Problems with even a minor aspect of their release process from one neuron to another have been linked to many brain disorders and nervous system diseases, including depression, autism, schizophrenia, dementia and epilepsy.

The role and symptoms of deficiency of some of these neurotransmitters are described in Figure 1.5.

Chapter 12, Our Brain and Lifestyle, discusses how certain foods boost the performance of neurotransmitters in our brain.

Our nervous system

The brain controls our nervous system, which regulates how we respond and adjust to the world around us.

Function of the nervous system

The nervous system has three main functions:

» *Sensory* – passing information from our senses to the central nervous system for processing.

» *Integrating* – using the sensory signals for decision-making or the formation of new memories.
» *Motor* – activating our muscles and glands.

There are two parts to our nervous system:

1 *Central nervous system* (brain and spinal cord).
2 *Peripheral nervous system* (cranial nerves branching from the brain, spinal nerves branching from the spinal cord and rest of the body).

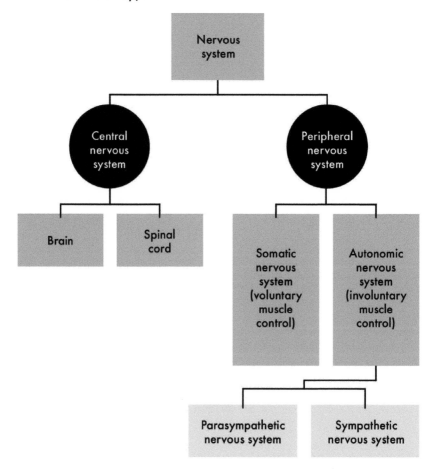

Figure 1.6: Our nervous system

Messages are carried between the central nervous system and the peripheral nervous system to activate the muscles and glands.

Central nervous system (CNS)

The **central nervous system** (CNS) is made up of the brain and the spinal cord and is composed of *grey and white matter*. **Grey matter** refers to the neurons and **white matter**

Figure 1.7: Our central nervous system

refers to the *axons*, or nerve fibres, that carry impulses between neurons. Axons are white because they are coated with a fatty substance called *myelin*, which gives them their colour. (The role of myelin is discussed later in this chapter.)

The spinal cord is a single continuous structure running from the brain, through the base of the skull and then down the spinal column.

The CNS controls our responses to the environment. It processes inputs that we receive through our senses and then communicates with the rest of our body by sending messages from the brain through the nerves branching off the spine that make up our peripheral nervous system (PNS).

Whenever we want to move our body, our CNS translates this intention into chemical and electrical messages that provide instructions for our muscles to activate.

If our CNS is injured or affected by disease, we can suffer permanent loss of function or disability.

Peripheral nervous system (PNS)

The **peripheral nervous system** (PNS) works with the CNS to process information from our environment.

Figure 1.8: Our peripheral nervous system

The PNS carries information to and from the CNS via our peripheral nerves and regulates our body temperature, blood pressure and thirst. Unlike the CNS, the PNS is not protected by bone. Damage to the CNS can cause damage to the whole body, whereas damage to the PNS is often localised.

There are two aspects to the peripheral nervous system:

» The *somatic nervous system* communicates with our senses and is involved in voluntary muscle movements, such as learning ballet or football. **Somatic nerves** come predominantly from the spinal cord and stimulate the contraction of skeletal muscles.

» In contrast, the *autonomic nervous system* regulates all the involuntary but life-critical activity of the internal organs and hormones – essentially everything internal that we never even think about. **Autonomic nerves** come from both

Parasympathetic nervous system	Sympathetic nervous system
Rest and digest	*Fight or fight*
The parasympathetic nervous system forms the body's *rest and digest* response when the body is resting and recovering.	The sympathetic nervous system forms the body's *fight or flight* response to acute, short-term stress.
It causes a decrease in heart rate and breathing and an increase in digestion.	It causes an increase in heart rate and breathing, higher levels of adrenaline and glucose, and a decrease in digestion.

the spinal cord and the brain and help to maintain homeostasis via two systems: the *parasympathetic nervous system* (*rest and digest*) and the *sympathetic nervous system* (*fight or flight*). See Figure 1.9 for more detail.

Body	Parasympathetic 'Rest and Digest'	Sympathetic 'Fight or Flight'
Eyes	Pupils constrict	Pupils dilate
Salivary glands	Saliva production increases	Saliva production reduces
Nose	Mucus production increases	Mucus production reduces
Heart	Heart rate slows	Heart rate increases
Lung	Bronchial muscles contract	Bronchial muscles relax
Stomach	Gastric juices and digestion increase	Digestion reduces
Liver	Normal function	Glucose increases
Kidneys	Urine increases	Urine decreases
Adrenal glands	Normal function	Adrenaline is released

Figure 1.9: Our autonomic nervous system

What happens when we activate the autonomic nervous system?

The two parts of the autonomic system (**parasympathetic** and **sympathetic**) are designed to work together in balance: when one part is working, the other stops. Too much activity on one side can lead to ill health.

Although our autonomic nervous system is continually on, functioning day and night, we are not conscious of it working on our behalf.

Our nervous system is vital for our ability to function in every way. It controls all the muscles, tissues and organs in our body. Our brain, spinal cord and peripheral nerves are coated with a protective layer of protein and fatty substances, called a *myelin sheath*. This coating process is known as *myelination*.

Myelin is essential for the proper working of our nervous system. When myelin is damaged, nerve impulses are affected, leading to diseases such as multiple sclerosis. We can promote the health of our myelin sheath by eating a healthy diet, as explained further in Chapter 12, Our Brain and Lifestyle.

Part 2: Impact on our daily life

Do women and men have different brains?

Figure 1.10: Women versus men – science or stereotypes?

There is considerable debate among researchers as to whether women and men have different brains. Scientists are divided over whether any differences in the brain are the result of our genetic make-up (*nature*) or whether, instead, they are the consequence of the family and culture we are raised in (*nurture*). In fact a recent study has even suggested that there are no real brain differences between the sexes, and that any brain differences emerge because of the significance we give them.[1]

Even so, from a biological point of view, men's brains are, on the whole, 10 to 12% bigger than women's brains. But a bigger brain does not necessarily mean a more intelligent brain! Men's brains tend to be bigger because they control a larger body mass and musculature than those of women. Although all human brains begin as female, there is a release of hormones that then determines the sex of the foetus. Around six weeks after conception, the brain of the male foetus will experience a surge of testosterone, which stimulates growth of the *hypothalamus*, the area of the brain that produces and controls our hormones.

The male brain produces more serotonin than the female brain. This may explain why there are more incidences of depression in women. However, there is an amino acid called *tryptophan* that stimulates serotonin production in the brain and is found in dark chocolate, among other foods.

The *anterior cingulate cortex*, which regulates thinking and emotion and is involved in detecting errors, is larger in the female brain. Dr Louann Brizendine calls this the 'worry-wort centre'.[2]

The *amygdala* and the *hypothalamus*, which are involved in the body's response to fear and danger, are sensitive to *testosterone* and they both grow larger in young men. This explains why many men are more attracted to competitive sport and why sexual desire can differ in young men and women.

Women have higher levels of *oxytocin* and tend to show greater levels of empathy than men, particularly during stressful periods. Men (especially young males) have higher levels of testosterone, which can suppress oxytocin levels.

Although the notion of pain is highly subjective it does appear that women are more sensitive to pain than men and suffer from pain-related conditions more frequently.[3] Men produce more *endorphins* than women, which could explain men's greater tolerance of pain. Chapter 2, Our Brain and Emotion, discusses endorphins in more detail.

Men's navigational skills and spatial judgement are more effective compared to women's. Men also consistently outperform women on mental rotation tasks unless they suppress their emotions, in which case they perform identically.[4] These differences have been linked to both men's higher levels of testosterone[5] and a larger male parietal lobe.[6]

Figure 1.11: Some differences between the sexes

One of the biggest differences between male and female brains has been observed in the *hippocampus*, which stores personal memories (explained in more detail in Chapter 3, Our Brain and Memory) and is engaged in processing memories into words. The hippocampus is sensitive to the female hormone oestrogen and grows faster and larger in young women. This may explain why women generally excel at remembering words, objects, pictures and faces.

Magnetic resource imaging (MRI) scans have shown that women have more connections in the corpus callosum that connects the two hemispheres, integrating information from both sides.[7] However, it is worth mentioning that the role of the corpus callosum has been much debated, with other studies claiming that any male/female differences are spurious or insignificant.

Diffusion tensor imaging (DTI) has also looked at pathways connecting the different regions of the brain in men and women. As shown in Figure 1.12, men's and women's brains are wired differently. Men's brains (shown in blue) are structured to facilitate front-to-back connectivity, moving between perception and decision-making. Women's brains (shown in orange) are wired more laterally, between the left and right hemispheres, suggesting that women have greater communication between logical analysis and intuition.

Figure 1.12: Men's and women's brains are wired differently

Credit: Dr Ragini Verma, *Proceedings of the National Academy of Sciences*[8]

It is nevertheless important to note that these differences emerge only after adolescence, which bolsters the notion that our brains are malleable and adaptable, particularly during childhood.

Male/female differences may therefore develop or be encouraged over time, as boys and girls are treated differently within the cultures in which they are raised.

Why are both nature AND nurture important?

We each represent a unique combination and interplay of factors, acquired from early childhood and life experiences, together with our genetic blueprint or inherited tendencies.

And so, even though we may be born with a physiological or psychological predisposition, our upbringing, especially during the early years, plays a critical role in determining whether certain behavioural traits will emerge or remain dormant.

This means that, while male/female biological differences have been observed through various studies, both nature *and* nurture play a combined role in establishing how we develop. Because the brain is a muscle, which like other muscles in our body needs to be kept active, it is strengthened or weakened through reinforcing or reducing certain patterns of brain activity. Throughout our life, we can continue to shape our brain by learning a range of skills, embracing new ideas and meeting different people.

What difference does being right- or left-handed make?

Most of us have a dominant hand that we use. We live in a right-handed world, with only around 10% of the total human population being left-handed. There are a number of theories that attempt to explain why this is the case, one of which is that right-handed dominance is an evolutionary adaptation that has been passed down over time.

Culture plays a significant role in determining which hand we use; for example, certain religions do not allow the left hand to be used for eating food or for ceremonial rituals.

Even though the hemispheres control our body diagonally, this does not mean that left-handed people are necessarily more *right-brained* or more creative, or that right-handed people are more *left-brained* or more logical. The complex way in which the hemispheres work together cannot be explained by simply saying that we are governed by either one side or the other.

Most of us may naturally have a preference towards one side and we are influenced by the way we are taught and tested. For example, a large number of education systems cater more for the left hemisphere, focusing on analysis and logic rather than on creativity and the arts.

But in reality, we all benefit from the combined functioning of both hemispheres.

Why teenagers do not think like adults

Teenagers' brains are wired differently to those of adults. One of the biological explanations for this is that their brains are not fully formed in the frontal lobe region; hence teenagers lack the necessary connections to help them think ahead and understand the consequences of an action. And yet we often expect teenagers to make important decisions regarding their education and future at a time when they are least equipped to do so.

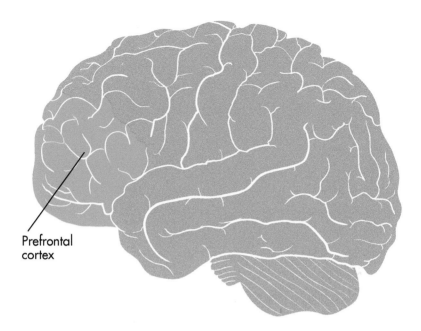

Prefrontal
cortex

Figure 1.13: The prefrontal cortex

The prefrontal cortex coordinates our brain and body and our higher-level, executive functioning: judgement, personality, impulse control, reasoning, long-term planning, intellect, mood, social skills, conscience and empathy. The prefrontal cortex continues to be remodelled during adolescence and is not fully formed until around the age of 25.

This is why teenagers often exhibit even poorer decision-making skills than they did when they were children. Dominant in the teenage brain is emotion and, with it, impulsive and risk-taking behaviour. Teenagers are at greater risk of death or injury than children. In fact, the rate of death by injury for teenagers between the ages of 15 to 19 is about six times that of the rate when they were aged between 10 and 14.

As a protective measure against the teenage propensity to become distracted or engage in risky behaviour, particularly in front of peers, Ford's MyKey system is designed for parents to limit the speed at which their children drive. The system interfaces with the computer systems on board and places restrictions on drivers. Speed is not the only restriction; stereo volume can be limited as well.

During our adolescent years, our neural connections grow and any connections that we do not use are pruned to help the brain become more efficient. This is a process called *synaptic pruning*.

At the same time as this synaptic pruning takes place, myelination occurs. As explained earlier in this chapter, the process of myelination coats our nerves with a protective fatty substance called myelin, which facilitates the transmission of signals between neurons. As the teenage brain remodels itself, the remaining connections are now able to communicate with each other with more efficiency and speed.

We mature as our brain improves its ability to integrate and transfer information between its different regions, and as a result, we are able to control our emotions and impulses more consistently.

Part 3: Stories and top tips

Was Einstein's brain different?

The brain of Albert Einstein has been the subject of much debate. Scientists have been intrigued to know whether Einstein had a brain different to the general population.

Seven and a half hours after his death, Einstein's brain was removed by scientists who then studied its structure. They discovered that it had a greater number of connections than the brains of other people of a similar age, suggesting that Einstein had continued to exercise his brain, hence delaying the degeneration that would normally occur during the ageing process.

The main difference in Einstein's brain was in an area of the parietal lobe known as the inferior parietal region, used for spatial awareness, mathematical thought and motor imagery. This region was so developed on both sides that his brain was 15% wider than other brains.

As well as enlarged parietal structures, Einstein's brain had a thicker corpus callosum connecting the two hemispheres, particularly in an area called the *splenium*, which facilitates communication between all four of the brain's lobes.[9]

Einstein's genius was therefore likely to have been a result of both a well-functioning brain and constant mental challenges throughout his lifetime.

Should young children head footballs?

There is now evidence to suggest that heading a football can leave younger players with lasting brain damage.[10] The US Soccer Federation has announced its intention to publish guidelines to limit the number of times children between the ages of 11 and 13 can take headers in training, and to ban them altogether for younger children.

Because children's heads are disproportionately large and their brains are not fully formed, there is more movement inside the skull. In addition to this, the brains of children and adolescents have not fully developed the protective myelin that covers neurons and consequently may be more vulnerable to head injuries.

The making of Vanessa-Mae

In 2008 a BBC programme called *The Making of Me* explored the nature/nurture debate through examining whether the famous violinist Vanessa-Mae's talent was a result of either her birth or her upbringing.

Vanessa-Mae learned the violin from the age of 5 and practised daily for four hours. She has sold more than ten million albums and has performed on the worldwide stage with many other renowned artists.

During the programme, Vanessa-Mae underwent a series of tests, including brain scans, heart monitors and psychometric assessments. She discussed the main influences in her life with geneticists and a psychologist. Throughout these discussions, Vanessa-Mae expressed how she had inherited her talent from her mother. But, at the same time, she accepted that her mother's encouragement to play the violin was a significant influence in honing her musical talent from early childhood.

As Vanessa-Mae claimed during the programme:

'Kids can be born with potential but unless it's encouraged – pushed, even – I don't think it will ever come to fruition.'

Balance your neurotransmitters in order to regulate your wellbeing and overall mood. Neurotransmitters are essential to our psychological and physical health. Chapter 12, Our Brain and Lifestyle, offers ideas for how to boost neurotransmitter imbalances through sleep, exercise and food.

Recognise, utilise and celebrate any male/female differences around you. Our evolution has depended on the appropriate dynamic between male and female characteristics. We all have something to offer and can complement each other well.

Activate your brain and challenge it regularly with mental exercises, memory games and new ideas. This will help keep your brain agile. A connected brain is a healthy brain and if you do not use your brain you will weaken its connections in those areas. The more you learn, the more connections you will create.

Invest time and effort in practising what you would like to become good at. Becoming an expert at any activity involves a great deal of dedication. There are no shortcuts!

Nourish your brain with the right environment and people around you. Make sure you are surrounded with people who believe in you and want the best for you. How you nurture your brain is as important as the brain you are born with. The influences you give your brain will affect changes to its structure and function throughout your lifetime.

References for Chapter 1

1 Joel, D. et al. (2015) 'Sex beyond the genitalia: the human brain mosaic', *Proceedings of the National Academy of Sciences*, October, 15468–73

2 Brizendine, L. (2010) *The Female Brain*. London: Transworld Publishers

3 Fillingim, R.B. et al. (2009) 'Sex, gender and pain: a review of recent clinical and experimental findings, *Journal of Pain*, May, 447–85

4 Fladung, A. & M. Kiefe (2016) 'Keep calm! Gender differences in mental rotation performance are modulated by habitual expressive suppression', *Psychological Research*, November, 985–96

5 Pintzkaa, C.W. et al. (2016) 'Changes in spatial cognition and brain activity after a single dose of testosterone in healthy women', *Behavioural Brain Research*, February, 78–90

6 Koscik, T. et al. (2009) 'Sex differences in parietal lobe morphology: relationship to mental rotation performance', *Brain Cognition*, November, 451–59

7 Ardekani, B.A. et al. (2012) 'Sexual dimorphism in the human corpus callosum: an MRI study using the OASIS brain database', *Cerebral Cortex*, August, 2514–20

8 Verma, R. et al. (2013) 'Sex differences in the structural connectome of the human brain', *Procedings of the National Academy of Sciences*, January, 823–28

9 Weiwei, M. et al. (2013) 'The corpus callosum of Albert Einstein's brain: another clue to his high intelligence?', *Brain*, September, 1–8

10 Di Virgilio, T.G. et al. (2016) 'Evidence for acute electrophysiological and cognitive changes following routine soccer heading', *EBioMedicine*, November, 66–71

'The best and most beautiful things in the world cannot be seen or even touched. They must be felt with the heart.'

Helen Keller

World-famous deaf–blind speaker and author (1880–1968)

2: OUR BRAIN AND EMOTION

About this chapter

Emotions drive our behaviour and shape our responses to what is happening around us. They enable us to take action, make decisions, connect and communicate with other people and build meaningful relationships. Emotions can be short-lived or can last a lifetime.

Emotions have played a valuable role in our survival as a species. Being able to understand emotional displays in others informs us how to adapt our behaviour appropriately.

This chapter explains why our brain is wired to produce a spectrum of emotions, how we read emotions in others, why emotion and memory are closely linked, and how emotions influence our decisions.

Part 1: The science explained

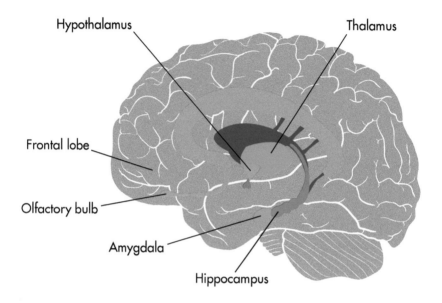

Figure 2.1: Our emotional circuitry

Our brain's emotional circuitry

The emotional circuitry in our brain is commonly known as the *limbic system*, which is situated predominantly in the temporal lobe. The name comes from *limbus*, the Latin word for 'border', and the word's usage has been attributed to a scientist called Paul Broca, who discovered the area around 150 years ago.

The main structures comprising the limbic system surround and interact with the *hypothalamus*; they are the *amygdala*, the *hippocampus* and the *thalamus*. The *prefrontal cortex* is also considered part of the limbic system because, although housed in the frontal lobe, it interacts with the rest of the limbic structures.

Limbic structure	Function
The hypothalamus	Regulates homeostasis (our internal balance) and is one of the most active parts of the brain. The hypothalamus works with the **pituitary gland** to activate our endocrine system or hormonal release throughout the body. Together these constitute our master gland and drive our responses.
The amygdala (named after the Greek word for *almond* because of its shape)	Activates in response to threats, although in recent years the amygdala has been linked to intense positive emotions as well.[1] The amygdala labels an event emotionally relevant or important based on past experience. It receives information from the thalamus and communicates with the hypothalamus to stimulate our stress hormones, adrenaline and cortisol. When our amygdala is stimulated, it can turn a calm demeanour into aggressive or fearful behaviour. When the amygdala is damaged or destroyed, fear is not registered at all.
The hippocampus (named after the Greek word for *seahorse* because of its shape)	Converts experiences into personal or autobiographical (*episodic*) memories. If the hippocampus is damaged, we cannot build new memories and can only rely on memories from the time before the damage occurred. This is one of the most plastic areas of the brain and the only region where we can grow new neurons.
The thalamus	Receives information from our senses – apart from our sense of smell – to the rest of the brain. Because smell (via our **olfactory bulb**) bypasses our thalamus, it is our strongest sense. The thalamus also regulates sleep, alertness and wakefulness. For example, when we need to sleep, the thalamus shuts off signals from the senses, thereby allowing us to rest.
The frontal lobe	Plays a critical role in our capacity to modulate emotions. This is the newest and most evolved part of the human brain and works together with the rest of the limbic circuitry: the frontal lobe interprets situations and then tells the limbic circuitry to produce the appropriate emotion.

Figure 2.2: Limbic system structure and functions

Why do we have emotions?

We all know what it is like to experience emotions. Many of us feel a multitude of emotions in one day. Some emotions help us, while other emotions can make a situation far worse.

Emotions are subjective. Different events may evoke different emotions in us, depending on our background and personality. For example, giving a presentation may be an enjoyable experience for some, but a source of intense anxiety for others.

Emotions also help us communicate with other people and recognise how another person is feeling, too. When we are more aware of our own emotional state, we are often better able to read the emotional state of others.

Equally, our emotions can often affect the way that other people feel; we do not always realise how contagious emotions are.

What exactly is emotion?

The word *emotion* is derived from the Latin word *emovere*, meaning 'to disturb'. Emotion therefore represents a change. This change has a cognitive component (the label we give to how we feel – such as *happy* or *sad*) and a physiological component (bodily changes such as increased heart rate or quickness of breath).

An emotion is often followed by an action. If we are sad, we may choose to be alone or find someone to talk to; if we are afraid, we may avoid a dangerous situation or threat; if we are angry, we may confront the source of our anger.

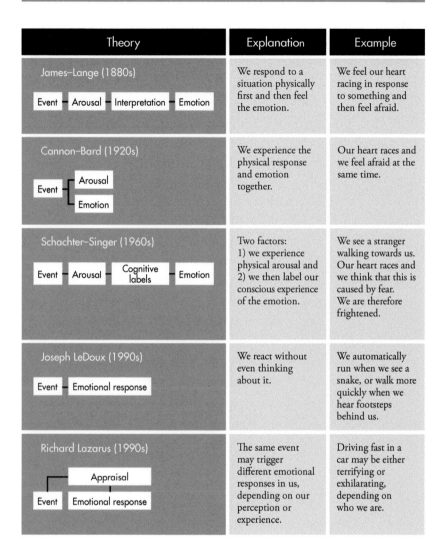

Theory	Explanation	Example
James–Lange (1880s) Event – Arousal – Interpretation – Emotion	We respond to a situation physically first and then feel the emotion.	We feel our heart racing in response to something and then feel afraid.
Cannon–Bard (1920s) Event ⊂ Arousal / Emotion	We experience the physical response and emotion together.	Our heart races and we feel afraid at the same time.
Schachter–Singer (1960s) Event – Arousal – Cognitive labels – Emotion	Two factors: 1) we experience physical arousal and 2) we then label our conscious experience of the emotion.	We see a stranger walking towards us. Our heart races and we think that this is caused by fear. We are therefore frightened.
Joseph LeDoux (1990s) Event – Emotional response	We react without even thinking about it.	We automatically run when we see a snake, or walk more quickly when we hear footsteps behind us.
Richard Lazarus (1990s) Appraisal / Event – Emotional response	The same event may trigger different emotional responses in us, depending on our perception or experience.	Driving fast in a car may be either terrifying or exhilarating, depending on who we are.

Figure 2.3: Comparing theories of emotion

The neuroscientist Dr Joseph LeDoux has influenced much of our understanding about the origins and purpose of emotions.[2] He explains that our emotional responses are hard-wired into the brain's circuitry and believes that emotion can trigger an instinctive reaction without the need for a conscious thought.

This means that, even when we think we are being rational, we are in fact being emotional.

Over the years, researchers and theorists have debated the exact dynamic or chronology of the cognitive and physiological elements of emotion. But all agree that emotion involves a change to both our physical and our mental state.

The importance of endorphins

The word *endorphin* is derived from two words: *endogenous* (meaning 'from within') and *morphine* (a painkiller). An endorphin is therefore essentially an internal painkiller.

Endorphins block the pain receptors in our body, which is why they are also known as *happy chemicals*. When we release endorphins, we experience a feeling of positive wellbeing or euphoria.

Endorphins are produced when we exercise, laugh or are in love – and also when we eat spicy food! We have 20 different types of endorphins, which are all important for the healthy functioning of our body.

As well as blocking our pain receptors, endorphins help to reduce anxiety and depression. They are also a natural relaxant and help us to sleep. In fact the word *morphine* is derived from Morpheus, the Greek god of sleep.

Endorphins also heighten our enjoyment of experiences, normalise blood pressure and enhance our immune system.

How can we read emotions in others?

 Our brain is wired to look for *similarities* rather than *differences* in other people so that we can easily identify people who are like ourselves. This tendency may have originated from a survival instinct: we feel safer when we are with people who are just like us, while people who are different may pose a threat to our existence.

Over the last 20 years, neuroscientific discovery has shed light on a system in the brain that enables us to *read* what other people are thinking and feeling.[3] This system is made up of *mirror neurons* or nerve cells that respond equally when we do something ourselves or when we observe someone else performing the same action.

For example, if we are drinking a cup of coffee, specific neurons activate to help us see the cup, move the cup to our mouth, taste the coffee, recognise it as coffee and then decide to continue drinking it, based on whether we like coffee or not. Simply the act of watching someone else drink a cup of coffee activates some of those same neurons – the two brains mimic each other.

 Our mirror neurons are therefore our *circuits of empathy*. They explain how we read emotions, decode facial expressions, understand other people and determine their intentions. Our mirror neurons enable us to see the world from another person's perspective; we even start to feel how they feel. This is why many of us cry when we see something sad on the television, and it is also why, when someone smiles at us in a genuine way, we find it hard not to smile back.

One of the best examples of how mirror neurons work is when we see someone yawn. We all know that yawning is highly contagious and scientists believe that it is a primitive expression of empathy.[4] When we see someone else yawn, our mirror neurons activate strongly, making us want to yawn too. When we have an emotionally close relationship with someone yawning, it is even more infectious.

And so, on a neurological level we can strongly identify with the people closest to us. In other words, when we observe suffering or pain in those we love, our brain registers pain as if we were experiencing the discomfort ourselves. This applies to both social pain and physical pain.

We need to read emotional expression

Our face is the main vehicle that we use to express emotion. We have 42 muscles in the face, which enable us to display a huge range of emotional variations.

Our brain is naturally designed to read faces. In fact, we have an area of the brain called the *fusiform face area* (FFA) that is dedicated to reading facial expressions. When we learn to read the emotional messages in someone else's face we become more aware of how we are feeling ourselves.

Paul Ekman, Professor Emeritus at the University of California, San Francisco, is an expert in facial expressions and gestures.[5] Since the 1970s, Professor Ekman and his colleagues, Wallace Friesen and Carroll Izard, have been examining emotional expressions around the world to determine if a smile in one country is the same as a smile in another country.

Based on their discovery that everyone reflects happiness and other emotions through the same facial features, Professor Ekman's team have developed the first and only comprehensive tool for objectively measuring facial movement and micro-expressions – the Facial Action Coding System (FACS). This system became well known via the television series *Lie To Me*.

The emotions that are universally recognised around the world are: anger, joy, surprise, disgust, sadness and fear.

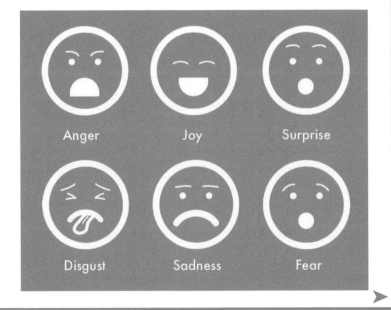

Anger   Joy   Surprise

Disgust   Sadness   Fear

The fact that there is consistency across diverse cultures suggests that our basic emotions are indeed instinctive.

More recently, a study has highlighted that there are actually 21 distinct facial expressions of emotion that we use regularly.[6] In addition to the six universally recognised emotions there are 15 expressions of *compound emotions*, which are constructed by combining different emotion categories, such as happily surprised or disgustedly angry.

The more time we spend with people and really focus on them, the better we are able to pick up the range of emotions that register on their face, even if these emotions are signalled as micro-gestures or subtle indications of a feeling.

Our ability to read emotional expression and connect with people develops from an early age, and interaction with others is critical for our emotional development. We rely heavily on picking up facial cues to establish an emotional connection with other people. By doing this, we enter into an unspoken reciprocal arrangement whereby we validate each other's words and gestures through both our verbal and non-verbal responses.

Effective communication therefore depends on our success in reading emotional cues from other people.

The Still-Face Experiment was first demonstrated to colleagues in 1978 by Edward Tronick, Director of the Child Development Unit and Distinguished Professor at the University of Boston.[7]

The experiment has been repeated a number of times and all replicated studies reinforce that young babies need emotional feedback from others and become quickly withdrawn and frustrated if they do not receive it.

Professor Tronick described how an infant after only three minutes of exposure to a non-responsive mother becomes confused, withdrawn and distressed and makes repeated attempts to resume a normal pattern of interaction.

Nowadays, the Still-Face Experiment is used to investigate attachment styles, cultural differences, autism, deaf children, infants with Down's syndrome and the impact of maternal depression.

Why are women faster than men at identifying emotions?

Researchers have demonstrated that women are faster at processing and differentiating between emotional expressions than men.[8] The male brain, it seems, has to work harder to evaluate emotion in others.

A study using magnetic resonance imaging (MRI) divided participants into three groups:[9]

1 Women
2 Men
3 Men with Asperger's syndrome (a disorder that impairs the ability to understand others)

All three groups were shown faces with different expressions and asked to decide whether those faces looked trustworthy, approachable or intelligent.

Their responses were timed and as they gave their answers their brains were scanned to see which areas of the brain were activated.

Both groups of men (those with and without Asperger's syndrome) experienced greater blood flow to the part of the brain responsible for social function, suggesting that they had to work harder than the women to read the facial expressions.

Those with Asperger's syndrome showed greatest brain activity, suggesting that they had to work the hardest.

Evolutionary psychologists suggest that males and females are wired differently because of distinct social roles that have evolved over time: men are able to detach from emotion and stay calm in a crisis, whereas women need to be able to detect emotion in order to respond to younger family members and nurture people around them.

Simon Baron-Cohen, Professor of Developmental Psychopathology at the University of Cambridge, explains how sex differences in emotional connection may be perceived. He suggests that the male brain is more systemising than empathising (S>E) and the female brain is more empathising than systemising (E>S).[10]

According to Professor Baron-Cohen men are better at working out how systems operate, such as repairing an engine (systemising), while women are better at working out others' feelings (empathising).

Professor Baron-Cohen also believes that an *extreme male brain* is one that is very good at systemising but very poor at empathising, and this may be connected to the condition known as autism – a condition that tends to affect more men than women.

Scientists have also examined the effect of *testosterone* on emotional sensitivity. Testosterone is a hormone that makes us more logical, rational, goal-oriented and more prone to aggressive behaviour. Men have higher levels of testosterone than women.

Testosterone also suppresses the effects of *oxytocin*, which helps us form bonds of trust with others. It seems that even small amounts of testosterone can prevent us from identifying emotions and even alter the connections between regions of the brain involved in emotional processing.[11]

However, the issue of sex differences in an emotional context is still quite controversial: many social scientists argue that any distinction we see is largely the result of stereotyping and the expectations placed on male and female roles in society.

Why is our brain designed for fear?

Much of our brain is devoted to the human fear response. Fear has effectively kept us alive as a species. If we were fearless, we would not have learned to avoid danger.

Fear has an immediate and dramatic effect on our physical state: our heart rate increases, breathing quickens and stress hormones are released. We learn to be frightened quickly and early on in our lives – and the effects of fear can often be enduring. For this reason, fear continues to be one of our most researched emotions.

The regions of the brain that govern our fear responses and memories are the amygdala and the hippocampus, two brain structures that were mentioned earlier in this chapter. They work together to stimulate our response to threat and prepare our body accordingly.

When we experience any threat or danger, the amygdala helps us to store this information so that we avoid the threat or danger in the future. The hippocampus remembers the context or location of the threat. Both the hippocampus and the amygdala activate as a warning signal when we find ourselves in a new situation that has similarities to a past event.

Why do psychopaths not feel fear?

The term *psychopath* (literally, 'suffering of the mind') was first used in 1900, to describe people who appeared outwardly normal but who also exhibited a lack of morality or conscience. In 1930, the term was changed to *sociopath* (meaning 'suffering of society') to indicate the harm that these people could inflict on others. Nowadays, both terms are often used interchangeably and generally describe the same personality traits.

The closest mental condition to psychopathy is *antisocial personality disorder*, which is described in the fourth edition of the *Diagnostic and Statistical Manual of Mental Disorders* (DSM IV), a reference guide used by psychologists and psychiatrists to categorise and diagnose mental illness. The current approach to defining psychopathy and its related terminology is based on a checklist of criteria, the most commonly used of which is the *Psychopathy Checklist Revised* (PCL-R) developed by Robert Hare, Professor Emeritus at the University of British Columbia.

The PCL-R describes psychopaths as showing emotional detachment and a lack of empathy. A number of studies have demonstrated psychopaths' inability to detect expressions of fear in the faces of other people.[12]

Brain imaging has also linked abnormalities in psychopaths' amygdalae with their inability to process fear, but not anger.[13] The fact that the amygdala is activated whenever we feel threatened suggests that psychopaths do not feel a sense of danger – which may lead to increased risk-taking. This is supported in a 2016 analysis of studies dating back to 1806, all of which highlight how psychopathic individuals do not detect threats.[14]

Hallmarks of a psychopath

According to Professor Hare, signs of psychopathy include: superficial charm and emotional responsiveness, a grandiose estimation of self, the need for stimulation and impulsiveness, pathological lying, cunning and manipulativeness, lack of remorse or guilt, callousness and lack of empathy, a parasitic lifestyle, poor behavioural controls, early behaviour problems, lack of realistic long-term goals, irresponsibility, short-term relationships.[15]

Psychopaths will display insincere charm in order to manipulate people quickly. They use deception and mimicry, often adapting their views and reactions to whomever they are dealing with.

Professor Hare also warns that anyone can be taken in by a psychopath.

From a neurobiological perspective, the brains of psychopaths do not register empathy for pain in the same way as for most other people. One of the key areas of the brain linked to pain perception (the *insula*) is triggered in psychopaths when they consider their own pain, but fails to activate when other people are in pain. Individuals who are rated as highly psychopathic have even shown an increased response in the area of the brain associated with pleasure when asked to imagine pain in others.[16]

Part 2: Impact on our daily life

Why do emotions influence our decision-making?

Emotion and decision-making are deeply intertwined in the brain and are not separate or opposing processes. In fact, many of our decisions are instant and based almost entirely on emotion.

The research of neuroscientist Professor Antonio Damasio has been instrumental in helping us understand how emotions influence our behaviour – in particular, our decision-making.[17]

Professor Damasio studied people with damage to the brain's emotional circuitry. In addition to finding that they could not feel emotions he also uncovered that they are unable to make decisions. These people could describe, in rational terms, the actions that they knew they should be taking, but could not settle on a decision. They were unable to make even simple decisions, such as what to eat.

Emotions are therefore a key component of our decision-making process. They enable us to weigh up options, rule out the wrong ones and settle on a choice that will result (we hope) in a positive outcome.

We rationalise – but we are not rational!

When we make a decision, we are always looking for a way to satisfy a basic human urge to be happy. This is why many of our decisions are unconscious attempts at minimising the impact of negative feelings such as guilt or fear, while heightening the effect of positive feelings such as happiness and love.

This dynamic interrelationship between emotions and decisions means that we often make a quick decision based on an emotion. We then associate a new emotion with the decision we have just made.

But the strong influence exerted by our emotions over our thought processes means that our decisions are susceptible to error. And because many of our decisions are fast and instinctive, we often do not realise the full impact of this emotional interference.

To illustrate this point, Nobel Prize winner and Professor Emeritus at Princeton University, Daniel Kahneman, describes the brain as operating two contrasting systems:[18]

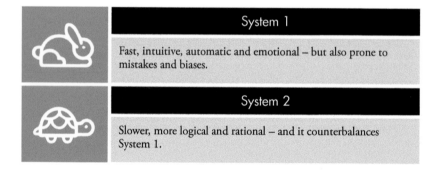

System 1
Fast, intuitive, automatic and emotional – but also prone to mistakes and biases.

System 2
Slower, more logical and rational – and it counterbalances System 1.

Figure 2.4: Kahneman's Systems 1 and 2

Professor Kahneman explains that most of us would like to think that we are engaging our System 2 more often than we actually do. However, System 2 is often slow and lazy to activate – and it sometimes even supplies evidence to support System 1's rapid conclusions.

In other words, we make a decision quickly and then justify it afterwards. We think we are being rational when we are actually just rationalising what has already been decided!

Example of System 1 thinking:

The following test, devised by Professor Shane Frederick of the Yale School of Management, illustrates how quickly we are drawn to the wrong answer:

If it takes 5 machines 5 minutes to make 5 widgets, how many minutes does it take 100 machines to make 100 widgets?

Intuitively we reach for the wrong answer (100 instead of 5 minutes in this case) and do not slow down to think and make the correct calculation.

Why do fear and anger colour our judgement?

Fear feeds off uncertainty. We worry when we do not know something, and then we often expect the worst. We may turn to anger to give us the confidence to act and take risks.

The problem with anger is that it can also make us oversimplify a situation and become more polarised and judgemental in our thinking.

In 2003 a study was conducted by Professor Jennifer Lerner at Harvard about the impact of emotions on decision-making. The study compared two groups:[19]

Group 1 was asked to read a news story about anthrax mail-threats (designed to instil fear)

Group 2 was asked to read an account of celebrations by some people in Middle Eastern nations related to the 9/11 attacks (designed to elicit anger)

Those in Group 2 (who were made to feel angry) voted for tougher penalties to be imposed than those in Group 1 (who were made to feel fear).

Another study has demonstrated that just by looking at angry facial expressions we are more likely to stereotype and condemn others.[20]

Of course this has important implications for our interactions with others. The emotional expressions that we wear ourselves, and those we read on the faces of those around us, seep into the judgements and assumptions we make on a daily basis.

By slowing down our thinking, we may be able to stall our early responses and come to a more considered and balanced view. And even if our first response is correct, we nonetheless always benefit from a period of reflection or a second opinion.

Why are emotional memories so vivid?

 When we have an emotional experience, the amygdala is involved in how this experience is stored and then remembered. The amygdala labels the memory as emotionally significant, and heightens both our visual perception and our sensory response to it.[21] The amygdala therefore increases the intensity of the memory – rather like increasing its brightness and volume in our brain.

But how we experience something is not always how we remember it. Even though an emotional memory may be more vivid than our other memories, we do not recall an exact replica of our experience.

The amygdala's role is to give us the big-picture view but not much else. From an evolutionary point of view, thinking about the detail may have slowed us down and cost us our life. So the amygdala leaves the peripheral detail out – and we often fill this detail in ourselves later.

So while the intensity of the memory may give us confidence about what we have remembered, this confidence is not matched by accuracy or detail in our recall. We are even adamant that we have remembered details that did not actually happen! This is covered in more detail in Chapter 3, Our Brain and Memory.

Emotional memories also often have a physical element. When we store an emotional memory, the amygdala and hippocampus work together to stimulate the production of *adrenaline* and *cortisol* to produce a physical response. The hippocampus then stores the memory for future reference, as a fusion of the physiological and emotional experience.

This is why when we recall emotional memories, we may also reactivate the same original physiological response. Because we can remember emotional memories so strongly, any disturbing memories we have stored may resurface and affect daily life, as in *post-traumatic stress*. Research is ongoing in this field to help people cope with such memories in order to resume normal living.

What is our gut feel?

Much of what we do every day takes place below the level of conscious thought. For example, we do not think about how we walk, nor do we stop to think about how we eat or use our cutlery.

Performing some tasks automatically means that we are freeing up other parts of our brain to take on a new cognitive challenge. This is discussed in more detail in Chapter 4, Our Brain and Attention.

When our cognitive processes fall below the level of consciousness, we no longer think about them and they become second nature. They also become part of our System 1 thinking and form our *gut feel*.

We use our gut as a reference point for a great deal in our lives. We feel that we can trust it as our own personal database. And we rarely question it – instead we reinforce what we believe to be true and relevant. As a result, the world we observe around us is often a reflection of the world we carry within ourselves. In other words, we see things as *we* are, not as *they* are. This is explained in more detail in Chapter 6, Our Brain and Visual Perception.

Every time we have a new experience, we look for ways to strengthen our existing memories. When the memory has a strong emotional element, we fortify both the memory and its associated emotion every time we recall the memory.

Because from an early age we are constantly storing experiences, we do not always remember each experience. Rather we are left with their emotional residue, such as our likes and dislikes, often without knowing their root causes.

As Maya Angelou said:

> ## 'I've learned that people will forget what you said, people will forget what you did, but people will never forget how you made them feel.'

Emotional intelligence: think about how you feel

Emotional intelligence (EQ or EI) is a term first used by Professors Peter Salovey and John Mayer in 1990 to describe the ability to manage emotions and then to use this ability to guide behaviour.

Six years later, the psychologist Dr Daniel Goleman gave the concept widespread appeal in his book *Emotional Intelligence*, in which he divided emotional intelligence into four quadrants (see Figure 2.5) to highlight the key areas of focus.[22]

The thinking behind Dr Goleman's model is that if we understand our own and others' behaviour we can communicate more effectively and appropriately in any situation. But much of the time we tend not to wait for our emotions to pass to allow reason to intervene and lead us, and instead allow them to override our thoughts, which can exacerbate an already tense or difficult situation.

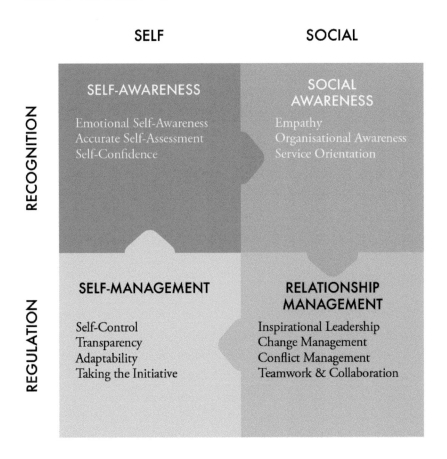

Figure 2.5: Daniel Goleman's model of emotional intelligence

Emotional intelligence therefore encourages us to mobilise our System 2 thinking and evaluate our feelings, rather than acting on them immediately.

Over the years, emotional intelligence has been cited as a hallmark for success in any domain and at any age. The topic is now being taught in schools, and some companies are using emotional intelligence criteria to hire and reward their people. When we observe and evaluate our emotions, we strengthen our ability to regulate our responses appropriately.

With technology dominating much of our social interaction today, we are at risk of misreading and misunderstanding each other. Email communication or electronic messaging may even create psychological numbing or emotional detachment, leading to a dwindling ability to empathise, connect and communicate in a genuine manner.

We therefore need to dedicate all the more time and effort to thinking about our emotions and those of the people around us.

Part 3: Stories and top tips

We are slaves to our emotions

We may be more aware of why we should monitor and manage our emotions in order to provide considered and appropriate responses, but we are still slaves to our emotions. We buy things we do not really need, we trust people without knowing enough about them, we become anxious at a sudden noise that we cannot immediately identify and we make decisions without considering hard evidence.

For example, after the September 11 tragedy in the United States, in which nearly 3,000 died, many people took to their cars to escape New York even though road travel has always had a higher fatality risk than air travel. The higher numbers on the roads inevitably led to many more deaths.

A dream that stirred a nation

On 28 August 1963 at the Lincoln Memorial, Washington D.C., Dr Martin Luther King spoke straight to the hearts of his audience.

The 'I have a dream' speech, delivered with confidence, presence and conviction, appealed to a basic need in people to belong and to reject isolation and the 'dark and desolate valley of segregation'.

By understanding how to manage his own emotions, while at the same time reaching people on an emotional level, Martin Luther King delivered an oration that stirred a nation and inspired hope with its promise of a better future. His words are still remembered today, having been passed down from generation to generation.

A display of affection that touched a child

In October 2013, Carlos, a six-year-old Colombian orphan, wandered on to the stage at the Vatican where Pope Francis was giving a speech about families. Carlos hugged the Pope's legs, sat in his chair and even played with the crucifix around the Pope's neck.

Even though this was a highly irregular incident, the Pope's response was one of empathy, tolerance and sensitivity. Displaying immense compassion, he seemed to understand the response the little boy needed; he patted Carlos on the head affectionately, as if he were his own child.

The dark side of emotion

The degree to which politicians successfully rouse and rile the public is expounded in Adam Curtis's 2016 film *HyperNormalisation*. Curtis takes us on a four-decade journey through political machinations that he claims have blinded us to what is normal – and his premise is that we can no longer see what is really there.

Voting behaviour is in itself an act of emotion and something that political scientists refer to as the 'voting paradox'.[23] This describes how the effort of voting is never matched equally by reward: each individual separately has no influence on the election outcome but we still vote because it is an expression of feeling. Political debate feeds our emotions and divides our opinions. Drew Westen's book *The Political Brain* describes voters as thinking with their 'guts'.[24]

The 2016 campaign for the United Kingdom to leave or remain in the European Union is an example of what is now being termed in the media 'emotional politics'. During the campaign, politicians on both sides were accused of influencing and directing voters' behaviour with scaremongering tactics rather than reasoned facts.

Sayeeda Warsi, the former chairman of the Conservative Party, resigned amid accusations that the *Leave* campaigners were resorting to messages of 'hate and xenophobia'.

'Politics of fear are very strong in persuading audiences who don't have much information to vote with their gut feeling, which is where rational discussions don't find a space.'

Ruth Wodak
Emeritus Distinguished Professor at Lancaster University

Leave supporters were incited to anger through references to immigration, loss of sovereignty and the drain on the National Health Service. The *Remain* campaign issued threats relating to uncertainty, insecurity and instability. On both sides, emotion held sway over rational thought.

And the emotion did not stop after voting had taken place. For some, the fear and anger that coloured the electorate's initial decision-making later turned to grief and regret. The aftermath even spawned new terms like 'Bregret' and 'Bregrexit'.

The 2016 American presidential election played to similar emotions. The arguments put forward by both presidential candidates seemed to be deliberate attempts to incite fear and, in particular, anger: anger against the other party, anger against the other candidate, anger against another country, anger against other people.

Positive emotions make us strong

 After suffering burnout in 2011, Ruby Wax enrolled in a Master's Degree at Oxford University in mindfulness-based cognitive therapy. Her book *Sane New World* discusses the need to live in the present and feel more positive and focused.[25]

Positive emotions change our brain's structure and function, enabling us to derive more pleasure from our experiences. When we savour a moment, whether it is through tasting something or listening to birdsong or laughter, we expand our brain's ability to appreciate and enjoy our experiences and surroundings. And importantly, we offset the scourge of our negativity bias, a topic which is explored in more detail in Chapter 7, Our Brain and Biases.

Positive emotions strengthen our system and enable it to flourish. But we have to work consciously and continually on generating these positive emotions.

Engage people by taking time to read the emotion in their faces. This will activate your mirror neurons, enabling you to connect with people on a deeper level. Give people visual feedback and facial cues to show them that you are listening and paying attention. Keep your mobile telephone out of sight: it is an unnecessary distraction and will detract from your ability to read the emotional expression of others.

Vocalise your emotions in order to manage communication with others. Learn to articulate how you feel and whether your immediate response is appropriate. Recognise and identify the source of your emotional triggers. Take the emotional temperature of a conversation and try to defuse any tension through your own language and behaviour.

Overrule your gut System 1 response by slowing down to think and assess what is happening. Our decision-making is fallible, emotional and easily influenced. By applying some logical systems of evaluation and using System 2 thinking, you will be able to judge situations more accurately and calmly.

Know how and why you may be swayed by the opinions, views and criticisms of others. Notice how often you find yourself being swept along by other people's fear and anger without even realising or questioning it.

Encourage different opinions and find people who do not always agree with you to be both a second pair of eyes and a second brain on an important decision you need to take. An opposing perspective or a challenging view helps us to become more considered and rational in our thinking.

References for Chapter 2

1 Bonnet, L. et al. (2015) 'The role of the amygdala in the perception of positive emotions: an "intensity detector"', *Behavioural Neuroscience*, 7 July [doi.org/10.3389/fnbeh.2015.00178]

2 LeDoux, J. (1999) *The Emotional Brain: The Mysterious Underpinnings of Emotional Life*. New York: Simon & Schuster

3 Rizzolatti, G. & L. Craighero (2004) 'The mirror-neuron system', *Annual Review of Neuroscience*, March, 169–92

4 Platek, S.M. et al. (2010) 'Yawn, yawn, yawn, yawn; yawn, yawn, yawn! The social, evolutionary and neuroscientific facets of contagious yawning', *Frontiers of Neurology and Neuroscience*, March, 107–12

5 Ekman, P. & W.V. Friesen (2015) *Unmasking the Face: A Guide to Recognizing Emotions from Facial Clues*. Cambridge, MA: Malor Books

6 Du, S. et al. (2014) 'Compound facial expressions of emotion', *Proceedings of the National Academy of Sciences USA*, April, 1454–62

7 Tronick, E. et al. (1978) 'Infants' response to entrapment between contradictory messages in face-to-face interaction', *Journal of the American Academy of Child and Adolescent Psychiatry*, Winter, 1–13

8 University of Montreal (2009) 'Women outperform men when identifying emotions', *Science Daily*, 21 October [www.sciencedaily.com/releases/2009/10/091021125133.htm]

9 Hall, J. et al. (2012) 'Social cognition, the male brain and the autism spectrum', *PLOS ONE*, December, 60 [doi.org/10.1371/journal.pone.0049033]

10 Baron-Cohen, S. (2003) *The Essential Difference*. London: Penguin Books

11 Bos, P.A. et al. (2016) 'Testosterone reduces functional connectivity during the "Reading the Mind in the Eyes" test', *Psychoneuroendocrinology*, March, 194–201

12 Hastings, M.E. et al. (2008) 'Psychopathy and identification of facial expressions of emotion', *Personality and Individual Differences*, May, 1474–83

13 Marsh, A. (213) 'What can we learn about emotion by studying psychopathy?', *Frontiers in Human Neuroscience*, April, 193–213

14 Hoppenbrouwers, S.S. et al. (2016) 'Parsing fear: a reassessment of the evidence for fear deficits in psychopathy', *Psychological Bulletin*, June, 573–600

15 Hare, R. (2016) 'This charming psychopath: how to spot social predators before they attack', *Psychology Today*, June [www.psychologytoday.com/articles/199401/charming-psychopath]

16 Decety, J. et al. (2013) 'An fMRI study of affective perspective taking in individuals with psychopathy: imagining another in pain does not evoke empathy', *Frontiers in Human Neuroscience*, September, 61 [doi.org/10.3389/fnhum.2013.00489]

17 Damasio, A. (2005) *Descartes' Error: Emotion, Reason and the Human Brain*. New York: HarperCollins

18 Kahneman, D. (2012) *Thinking Fast and Slow*. London: Penguin Books

19 Lerner, J. et al. (2003) 'Effects of fear and anger on perceived risks of terrorism: a national field experiment', *Psychological Science*, March, 144–50

20 Bodhausen, G.V. et al. (1994) 'Negative affect and social judgement: the differential impact of anger and sadness', *European Journal of Social Psychology*, January, 45–62

21 Todd, R.M. et al. (2013) 'Shared neural substrates of emotionally enhanced perceptual and mnemonic vividness', *Frontiers in Human Neuroscience*, 6 May [prepublished online 22 March; doi.org/10.3389/fnbeh.2013.00040]

22 Goleman, D. (1998) *Emotional Intelligence*. London: Bloomsbury

23 Klor, E.F. & E. Winter (2007) 'The welfare effects of public opinion polls', *International Journal of Game Theory*, February, 379–94

24 Westen, D. (2008) *The Political Brain: The Role of Emotion in Deciding the Fate of the Nation*. New York: Public Affairs

25 Wax, R. (2013) *Sane New World: Taming the Mind*. London: Hodder & Stoughton

'Memory is a great artist. For every man and for every woman it makes the recollection of his or her life a work of art and an unfaithful record.'

André Maurois

Author
(1885–1967)

3: OUR BRAIN AND MEMORY

About this chapter

Our memory serves an important protective function in our life. It provides us with a reference guide that helps us respond quickly to events and experiences.

Our memory is effectively our brain's data-storage unit and filing system. We access this stored data to help us interpret and compare new information that we take in via our senses.

For this reason, memory is a critical resource for us, and without it we would be lost. Our collection of memories effectively makes us who we are.

But memories for the same events do vary from person to person – we all choose to remember different aspects of our life's experiences.

This chapter explains how memory works in our brain, the different types of memory that we create, where these memories are stored, why memory is not always a reliable reference point and how we can improve our capacity to remember.

Part 1: The science explained

How do we research memory?

Memory is very complex and personal – and it is not an easy topic to research. Studies using a laboratory setting have been criticised on the grounds of low ecological validity, meaning that they cannot always be applied to a real-world environment. In addition to this, the questions used by researchers to prompt participants' memories can affect recall ability and accuracy, which is explained in more detail later in this chapter.

Over the years, however, scientists have been able to build a picture of how and where memory works in our brain. As well as the various studies that have been conducted, valuable insights have been obtained through incidents of brain trauma or brain damage.

Every new discovery brings us closer to a better understanding of our memory function.

How does memory work in our brain?

As we grow and mature, the neurons in our brain communicate and connect. Our memories are formed and then consolidated when certain connections are strengthened.

We are constantly connecting the new information that we receive through our senses with the details that we have already stored.

Memory is therefore both *reconstructive* and *constructive*: when we remember something we may add or delete detail to create a new version of our experience. And every time we access that same memory, we alter it slightly, so that over time it becomes markedly different to what actually happened in the first place.

 This is why our memories are never an exact replica of the event in question. Because we each attribute varying levels of emotional significance to the experiences we share with others, our memories of the same experience may differ.

The psychologist Professor Daniel Kahneman describes our two selves as the *experiencing self* and the *remembering self*.[1]

» The **experiencing self** operates in the present – in the *now* – with each moment lasting about three seconds.
» The **remembering self** represents how we *think* about the experience and what we keep from it.

The last moments of an experience can colour how we choose to remember the whole event. So even if our general experience has been pleasurable, an unpleasant occurrence towards the end will affect how we then remember it overall.

As Professor Kahneman explains, the remembering self is heavily influenced by our protective negativity bias: we are hard-wired to hold on to negative rather than positive experiences. Chapter 7, Our Brain and Biases, explores this in more detail.

How do we form memories?

When we receive information into our memory through our senses, we need to store it. This storage process is called *encoding* and it involves changing any incoming information into various formats.

There are three main formats:

	Visual (picture)
	We see something visual. Example: we see a person's name written down.
	Acoustic/auditory (sound)
	We hear something and repeat it back. Example: we try to pronounce a person's name.
	Semantic (meaning)
	We try to understand where something comes from and what it means. Example: we think about where a person's name is from.

Figure 3.1: How we encode information

The way that we encode and store this information affects later *retrieval*.

Encoding   Storage   Retrieval

If we make an effort to encode the same information through a number of different channels, we increase our chances of remembering it later.

For example, if we need to remember a person's name, we can see it written down (*visual*).

If we see it and then repeat it (*visual and acoustic*), we have a better chance of remembering it.

If we see it, repeat it (*visual and acoustic*) and then find out what the name means or where it comes from (*semantic*), we significantly increase the likelihood of remembering the name.

Figure 3.2: Different types of memory in our brain

Different types of memory

There are three basic memory types, as shown below. There has been considerable research into the relationship and differences between short-term and long-term memory.

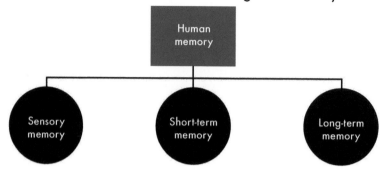

Figure 3.3: Different types of memory

Sensory memory

Sensory memory is the shortest element of memory and is a critical first step in storing information in short-term memory. The problem with sensory memory is that we forget much of what we see within less than a second. This rapid process of forgetting is known as *decay*.

Of all the senses, smell is probably the one most likely to result in longer-lasting memories. The *olfactory bulb* transmits olfactory (relating to smell) information from the nose directly to the *limbic circuitry* (*hippocampus* and *amygdala*), which is central to memory consolidation.

Figure 3.4: Smell is closely associated with emotional memory

Short-term memory (STM)

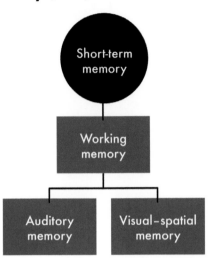

Figure 3.5: Short-term memory

Short-term memory (STM) refers to information held in our current consciousness and is very brief, lasting only a few (0–30) seconds.

Traditional theory has suggested that most adults can store between five and nine items in their short-term memory because of limited capacity. Seven is the number that is often quoted as our limit for storing single items.[2] We can observe this when we try to remember a list of words or numbers.

But when we group or *chunk* words or numbers together, we have a greater chance of remembering them, compared to

trying to remember an ungrouped or unchunked list of words or numbers. For example, we are more likely to remember chunked words like *night and day, don't look now* and *job well done* than a random list of words, such as *night, look, job, and, done, day, now, well.*

We store and retrieve short-term memory sequentially. This means that we will tend to recall words in the same sequence in which we encoded them.

If we do not actively pay attention to storing new information, we will lose it quickly. However, we can increase the duration of short-term memories by rehearsing and repeating any new information that we receive.

Working memory is part of STM and is the process whereby we continually focus on material for longer than STM alone will allow. Working memory plays an important role in concentration and following instructions. It activates an area of the frontal lobe, *the prefrontal cortex*, which is an energy-intensive part of the brain.

We hold information in our working memory so that we can quickly compare it to other information. Our working memory is particularly switched on by novel or unfamiliar information. In other words, our brain is naturally attracted to what is new!

There are two types of working memory: *auditory memory* (records what we hear) and *visual–spatial memory* (records what we see). Chunking in working memory helps us learn words and figures more easily.

Long-term memory (LTM)

In contrast to short-term memory, the capacity of our **long-term memory** (LTM) is thought to be unlimited. Information stored in our long-term memory can last a lifetime.

We store and retrieve long-term memory by association with previously stored information.

There are several different types of LTM:

Figure 3.6: Long-term memory

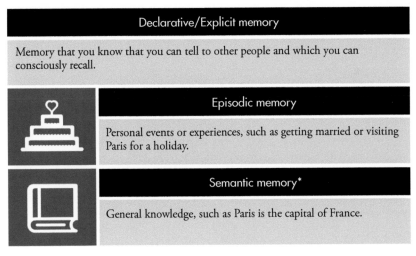

Figure 3.7a: Declarative memory

* Semantic memory is generally derived from episodic memory and may have had a personal association but, over time, sensitivity for certain events is reduced and it becomes generalised as factual knowledge.

Non-declarative/Implicit memory
Memory of what we can do or tasks we perform, often without thinking.

	Procedural memory
	Knowing how to ride a bicycle, drive a car, tie a shoelace or play a musical instrument. Typically acquired through repetition and practice.
	Priming
	Being influenced in a certain way by being exposed to another factor (behaviour, smell, temperature or language).
	Conditioning
	Responding to a light, sound or smell based on a previous experience (such as salivating when we see/smell our favourite food).

Figure 3.7b: Non-declarative memory

The motor cortex is involved in storing procedural memories

The frontal lobe stores semantic memories

The prefrontal cortex stores short-term memories

The amygdala plays a key role in forming emotional memories

The hippocampus forms and stores episodic and semantic memories

The cerebellum plays an important role in storing procedural memories

Figure 3.8: Memory types and brain structures

One of the best-known studies of memory has provided valuable insights into how memory is stored.[3]

An epilepsy patient who was referred to as H.M. had his hippocampus removed and was subsequently unable to form new personal and episodic memories. At the time, this outcome indicated that the hippocampus alone was involved in the formation of these memories. Later studies have since confirmed that the hippocampus is not the only structure implicated in memory formation; other surrounding structures, such as the amygdala, also play a key role in the construction of emotional and personal memories.

Even so, damage to the hippocampus does affect our ability to form lasting episodic memories. Alzheimer's Disease, which reduces hippocampal volume, is also characterised by episodic memory impairment.

By contrast, procedural memories do not appear to involve the hippocampus at all and are encoded and stored by the areas of the brain involved in motor control. This has been observed in cases of amnesia that result in loss of memory related to personal events, but which do not affect the ability to play the piano, for example.

Part 2: Impact on our daily life

Why do we remember what we remember?

Primacy/ Recency effect	We remember information that occurs first and last better than information that comes in the middle.
Von Restorff effect	We remember something that is noticeably different or new. This switches on our working memory. For example, we may not be aware of driving past sheep grazing in a field but we would certainly remember it if we passed a bright pink sheep!
Frequency effect	The more we repeat something, the better we will remember it.
Associations/ Mnemonics	When we associate or attach information to other information it becomes easier to remember. *Mnemonics* are memory devices that help us remember a list of facts. The word *mnemonic* is derived from the Ancient Greek word meaning 'relating to memory'. A mnemonic can take the form of a song, rhyme, acronym or image that is associated with the facts you want to remember. ➤

For example we can remember the colours of the rainbow like this:
– *Richard of York Gave Battle In Vain*
– **Red, Yellow, Green, Blue, Indigo, Violet**

The five tips at the end of each chapter in this book take the form of an acronym mnemonic to help you remember them.

Types of amnesia

Figure 3.9: Types of amnesia

There are two main types of amnesia, both of which may be caused by head injury, trauma or brain damage.

Retrograde amnesia An inability to retrieve memories of the past, before the onset of the amnesia.

Anterograde amnesia An inability to form new long-term declarative memories after the onset of the amnesia. However, non-declarative memories, such as procedural memories, may remain intact. This is explained in the stories section towards the end of this chapter. The amnesia featured in movies is usually anterograde amnesia.

A total loss of memory is known as *global amnesia. Transient global amnesia* may last for a few minutes or hours.

Our loss of very early childhood memories, known as *infantile amnesia*, has been explained by scientists as being due to our primary brain development and the rapid creation of many new neurons blocking access to old memories.

What memories are most memorable?

Emotional memories are often remembered with an intensity that is not matched by other types of memories. These memories were described in 1890 by William James[4] as:

> **'. . . so exciting emotionally as almost to leave a scar upon the cerebral tissues.'**

Memories that leave us with a strong and lasting impression are often referred to as *flashbulb memories*. The concept of flashbulb memories was first put forward in 1977 by psychologists Roger Brown and James Kulik, who described them as so emotionally important to us that they are captured as vividly and completely as a photograph.[5]

However, there has been an ongoing debate about how flashbulb memories are encoded in the brain. When strong emotion and memory collide, the amygdala is activated and influences the way the hippocampus registers the information, as discussed in Chapter 2, Our Brain and Emotion.

The problem with the amygdala's involvement is that it enhances the emotional elements of the memory but does so at the expense of peripheral detail. So even though we think we have remembered something clearly, much of the detail is often missing.

In January 1986, the day after the space shuttle *Challenger* had exploded just 73 seconds into its flight, leading to the deaths of its seven crew members, Ulric Neisser, Professor of Cognitive Psychology at Emory in the United States, asked his students to record what they were doing when they heard the news, whom were they with and where they were.[6]

Two and a half years later, Professor Neisser asked the same students the same questions. When the two sets of answers were compared there were very few similarities. Even though people were very clear about what they said they saw and remembered, their later memories were not true representations of what actually happened.

And so we can never be sure that someone else has remembered the same event in the same way that we have remembered it.

What affects our memory?

A number of factors can interfere with our ability to remember. Because the brain is so adaptive, it changes for the better or worse by virtue of the lives we lead.

Factor	Effect on memory
Sleep	Daily habits, such as exercise and sleep, can improve or worsen our memory. Lack of sleep can adversely affect the ability of our brain to strengthen our synaptic connections and boost our ability to remember. Research has also shown that a nap lasting just six minutes is sufficient to enhance memory function.
Food	Certain foods can help our memory function better. Foods that sustain a healthy heart will sustain a healthy brain. Oily fish (salmon, tuna, sardines, herring) are good sources of docosahexaenoic acid (DHA), a type of omega-3 fatty acid. Dark berries, such as blackberries, blueberries and cherries, are a rich source of anthocyanins, as are other flavonoids that may boost memory function. Walnuts and green tea improve working memory and reduce cognitive impairments. Vitamins B6 and B12 may also slow shrinkage in the hippocampus.
Exercise	A passive lifestyle is detrimental to brain health over time. Sitting for more than 20 minutes at a time increases our risk of diabetes and heart problems,[7] but it can also cause our brain to atrophy or shrink. Exercise improves oxygenated blood flow to the brain and stimulates the growth and connectivity of neurons in the hippocampus. In particular, taking exercise enables neurons to release a protein called brain-derived neurotrophic factor (BDNF), which directly benefits our ability to learn and remember. A study has shown that monkeys taking regular exercise learn tasks twice as quickly as monkeys that are sedentary.[8]
Stress	When we are stressed, anxious or depressed, we lose connections between neurons, thereby making memory formation and retrieval more difficult. When we are exposed to stressful situations over time, certain regions of our brain start to reduce in size, including our prefrontal cortex (needed for working memory) and our limbic regions (needed for emotional and episodic memory).[9] Stress also makes us more vulnerable to depression or addiction.
Smoking	Smoking impairs the blood supply to the brain and may also lead to lapses in memory. Studies show that smokers have problems with memory, compared with non-smokers.[10] Smoking may also cause certain proteins to accumulate in our brain, which then interfere with brain function and information processing.
Alcohol	It does not take much alcohol, consumed on a regular basis, to affect our memory function. Alcohol can prohibit blood flow to the brain and cause nerve damage. Recent research has shown that even two and a half drinks every day may accelerate memory loss by six years in middle-aged men.[11] No differences were observed between beer and wine: they have the same effects on cognitive function.

Figure 3.10: Factors affecting memory

Is the Internet making us stupid?

 We have access to unlimited information via the Internet. However, this *Google effect* has a downside because the availability of information means that the brain does not need to remember all the information we are exposed to. For example, we now forget details that in the past we would have memorised, and we no longer bother to commit to memory what we can look up or store instead. In effect, we are using our technological devices to store our long-term memories for us.

This phenomenon of forgetfulness is known as *digital amnesia*. A recent study claims, that 90% of us cannot even remember our children's or partner's telephone numbers.[12]

We seem to be losing the ability to reflect, deliberate and associate – all skills that our memory needs to encode and store for later retrieval. The steady stream of visual input from our electronic devices requires immediate responses, and our thinking skills are now being sacrificed in favour of endless and superficial short-term scanning and sifting. Researchers in Germany have found that people browsing the Web will spend less than ten seconds on each page.[13]

In his book *The Shallows*, Nicholas Carr describes a world of speed and superficiality that is breeding ignorance and changing the way we think and remember.[14]

Memory requires concentration and attention, and it is clear that the more we are bombarded with different distractions, the less we remember.

But it is not all bad news. Technological devices, such as video games, have increased our spatial awareness, our ability to attention-shift rapidly and our hand-to-eye coordination. And because our brain is so plastic, it has started to adapt in order to cope with our digital world.

Our recently acquired ability to shift quickly from one thing to another has come at the cost of other higher-level cognitive processes such as problem solving, creativity, reflection and critical thinking. This view is supported by Professor Patricia Greenfield, a developmental psychologist at the University of California, Los Angeles, whose research has analysed the impact of the Internet on the way students learn.[15]

Among the studies that Professor Greenfield refers to is one involving students who were given access to the Internet during class, compared with another set of students who were not given access. The Internet group did not process and remember the lecture as well as the students who did not have access to the Internet.

As Professor Greenfield states:

'The developing human mind still needs a balanced media diet.'

Technology is therefore changing the structure of our brain and the way that we process and remember information. But as some connections are strengthened in our brain, so others weaken.

 For example, our increasing reliance on satellite navigation (Satnav/GPS) is affecting our innate ability to navigate and orientate. When technology fails us we find that we are left with a diminished ability to think for ourselves. People who regularly use Satnav/GPS report that they no longer pay attention to their surroundings and find it harder to remember where they have been, compared to those who use maps.[16]

In 2015, Stephen Hawking warned of the threat of rapid technological advances that may well supersede human ability. He has been quoted as saying that artificial intelligence is:

'. . . either the best or the worst thing ever to happen to humanity.'

The impact of technology on our cognitive abilities is being hypothesised and debated globally. What is clear is that our world is changing exponentially around us and we need to consider carefully how we manage this transformation.

Use it or lose it

All memories grow weaker over time. In 1885, Herman Ebbinghaus called this the *Forgetting Curve*.[17]

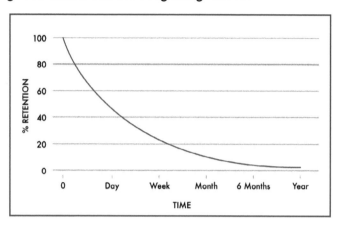

Figure 3.11: Ebbinghaus's Forgetting Curve

The more we revisit and recall memories, the more likely we are to retain them. And our memories strengthen with frequency of recall. If we make a deliberate effort to retrieve a memory at spaced intervals, we will have a better chance of holding on to it.

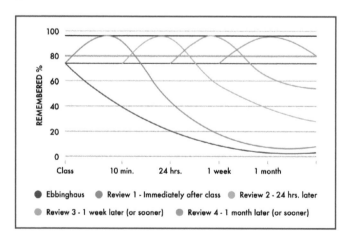

Figure 3.12: Overcoming the Forgetting Curve

When we remember something for a one-off purpose, such as an exam, and then do not retrieve it later, we often forget it as quickly as within a month. When we actively retrieve a memory, we then recreate and reinforce it.

Our brain also finds ways of linking memories together; for example, sleep can be a very helpful time to consolidate information we need to remember. If we try to encode a memory just as we are going to sleep, we have a better chance of remembering it later.

Lost and false memories

When we cannot remember something that we know we should know, it can feel very frustrating. This is called a *lost memory*. When we look for a route through to the memory via various associations or connections with the memory, it can often trigger the memory for easier retrieval.

Relaxation can prompt a lost memory to resurface. This can have both positive and negative consequences, as discussed in Chapter 10, Our Brain and Stress. While we often welcome the return of a memory that has proved elusive and hard to retrieve, the reappearance of certain repressed memories (for example, from childhood) may also cause anxiety. Accessing relaxed or meditative states in those with past trauma therefore needs to be handled carefully.

Sometimes our brain quickly stores the wrong information, creating a *false memory*. This may occur because it is easier for our brain to hold on to inaccurate or misleading data than to spend time analysing what we have heard. And because we remember it, we may then store it as truth. We are more likely to do this when fact and fiction are merged to form one story and we are unable to untangle the two.[18]

A false memory may also form if the memory is distorted by subtle cues that steer us in the wrong direction. As a consequence, we believe that we have clearly remembered something that never happened, which is discussed later.

How do we improve our memory?

Improving memory requires active and constant effort.
If we do not make a point of recalling and reviewing our memories, they will be lost to us as part of their natural decay.

Our brain works through making constant associations and we can increase these associations in different ways. We just need to keep our brains active. As the neuroscientist Dr David Eagleman says:

'Almost any silly suggestion can work. Drive home via a different route, brush your teeth with your opposite hand . . . the more senses you involve the better.'

Part 3: Stories and top tips

We do not remember accurately

Our memory for an event is affected and distorted by information we receive after the event has happened. This information is known as *after-the-fact information* and sometimes provides irrelevant detail which subsequently becomes incorporated into the earlier memory of the event.

This phenomenon has been observed in studies where people exposed to certain interview techniques go on to develop false memories based on the language and behaviour used by the interviewers. People even say they remember doing something that never actually happened. This is why eyewitness testimony, a key part of criminal investigation, is often unreliable.

A well-cited study by Dr Elizabeth Loftus and John Palmer highlights how the simple use of a verb can influence the recalled accounts of different eyewitnesses.[19]

In their experiment, participants watched a film in which two cars crashed into each other.

Participants were then randomly allocated to one of five groups and asked to answer some questions about the film. Each group had one particular question that

➤

differed slightly in its wording between the groups, such as:

'About how fast were the cars going when they **collided** with each other?'

'About how fast were the cars going when they **contacted** each other?'

'About how fast were the cars going when they **smashed** into each other?'

'About how fast were the cars going when they **bumped** into each other?'

'About how fast were the cars going when they **hit** each other?'

Those who were asked the question with the word *smashed* gave a higher speed estimate (40.8 mph) compared with *collided* (39.3), *bumped* (38.1), *hit* (34.0) and *contacted* (31.8). This study illustrates how language can have a distorting effect on memory and our estimates of speed.

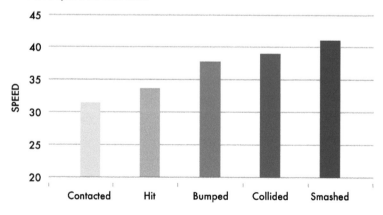

Estimated speed for verb used

A recent report, *Identifying the Culprit: Assessing Eyewitness Identification* (2014), is likely to challenge the validity and use of eyewitness testimony in the United States, particularly in the wake of wrongful convictions that have later been overturned using DNA evidence.[20]

A memory of ten seconds but a brilliant musician

In 1985, British conductor and musician Clive Wearing suffered one of the severest recorded cases of *anterograde amnesia* after a brain infection, herpes encephalitis. He was left with a memory span of between 7 and 30 seconds. However, his musical ability and much of his musical memory remained unaffected. Today he is still able to play the piano and read music.[21]

German neurologists have also been fascinated by the similar case of a professional cellist who suffered herpes encephalitis in 2005, lost his memory of simple detail but could still play his cello.[22]

Herpes encephalitis affects the temporal lobe, which houses our *episodic memory* (memory that is based on our past experiences and is therefore personal to us), whereas *procedural memory* (such as the memory of how to play music) remains intact because it is stored elsewhere in our brain.

For example, Clive Wearing plays the piano but does not remember that he can play; nor can he recognise his piano until he is told about it. He can, however, retrieve memories from his childhood and he remembers his wife, whom he knows he loves. Every time he sees his wife, he greets her with delight because he believes he has not seen her for a long time, even though she may have just left the room. Because he has no memory, he feels like he has just woken up from a coma.

As Wearing's wife, Deborah, explains, her husband's memory lasts for only a blink of an eye, with every new blink revealing a new view of the world:

'When the music stops he falls back into this abyss. He doesn't know anything about his life. He doesn't know anything that's happened to him ever in his life.'

How does Alzheimer's Disease affect long-term memory?

Alzheimer's Disease (AD) begins by affecting short-term memory. Because the symptoms are gradual and are sometimes confused with ageing they are not always reported early on. The person may just seem forgetful. But AD may be more successfully diagnosed, treated and controlled if these symptoms are recognised early.

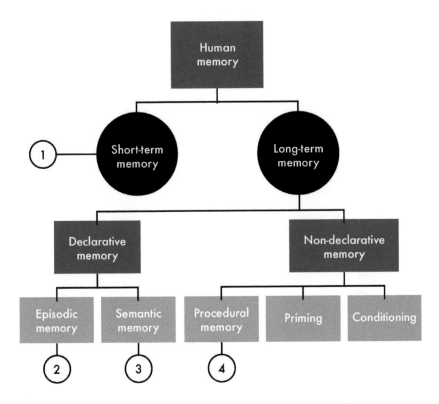

Figure 3.13: Order in which Alzheimer's Disease affects memory

Because short-term memory is essential for encoding information for long-term memory, over time people start to suffer from amnesia. They may not be able to store information or retrieve it. AD usually affects *episodic memory* (personal memories) first, then *semantic memory* (memory of words and general knowledge) and finally *procedural memory* (how to perform tasks or skills). This is highlighted in Figure 3.13.

In the early stages of AD, two proteins, *tau* and *beta-amyloid*, are involved. The tau protein, which normally supplies nutrients to the neurons, becomes tangled; nutrients are shut off, killing the neuron. Beta-amyloid forms deposits known as plaques, which impair communication between neurons.

The neurons eventually die and the hippocampus in particular starts to shrink, eroding the memories that have been stored and making the formation of new long-term memories impossible. This is why people suffering from AD lose a sense of who they are and how their life has been constructed.

Alzheimer's Disease is now the most common form of dementia, which is the umbrella term for a group of symptoms affecting cognitive tasks such as memory and reasoning. According to the World Health Organization, 47.5 million people around the world are now living with dementia. Awareness and an early diagnosis are critical to addressing this growing problem.

As the actress Carey Mulligan, the Alzheimer's Society's first Global Dementia Friends Ambassador, says:

'It's so important that everyone living with the condition is treated with the respect and dignity that they deserve. At the moment, there's not nearly enough awareness about what dementia is and as a society we all have a duty to change that.'

Sleep! This is so important for our memory function. Chapter 12, Our Brain and Lifestyle, discusses the optimum hours of sleep per age group. If you are suffering from lack of sleep short naps of between 10 and 30 minutes during the day have been found to boost and restore brainpower.

Test your brain with challenging cognitive exercises such as cryptic crosswords or memory games. Beat the Forgetting Curve by practising your recall and making associations. The best way to remember anything is to teach it to someone else!

Organise words or concepts with systems or devices, such as mnemonics that chunk information into a memorable format. Use different types of mnemonics to vary the way you encode information. The act of creating a mnemonic will help you remember the information.

Regulate your diet and include salmon, mackerel, tuna and other fish that are rich in heart-healthy omega-3 fatty acids, which are important for the normal functioning of neurons. Green tea, walnuts and vitamins E, D, B6 and B12 are also good for enhancing memory.

Exercise! The hippocampus, where we store personal memories, is able to grow new neurons through physical exercise and can even regenerate itself throughout our life (known as *neurogenesis*). Exercise also protects neurons from damage by increasing oxygen-rich blood flow to the brain.

References for Chapter 3

1   Kahneman, D. (2012) *Thinking Fast and Slow*. London: Penguin Books

2   Miller, G.A. (1955) 'The magical number seven, plus or minus two: some limits on our capacity for processing information', *Psychological Review*, May, 45–62

3   Squire, L. (2009) 'The legacy of patient H.M. for neuroscience', *Neuron*, January, 6–9

4   James, W. (1890) *The Principles of Psychology*. New York: Cosimo Inc.

5   Brown, R. & J. Kulik (1977) 'Flashbulb memories', *Cognition*, March, 73–99

6   Neisser, U. and N. Harsch (1992) *Phantom Flashbulbs: False Recollections of Hearing the News about Challenger. Affect and Accuracy in Recall: Studies of 'Flashbulb' Memories*. New York: Cambridge University Press, 9–31

7   Wilmott, E. et al. (2012) 'Sitting for protracted periods increases risk of diabetes, heart disease and death', *Science Daily*, October [www.sciencedaily.com/releases/2012/10/121015090048.htm]

8   Rhya, I.J. et al. (2010) 'Effects of aerobic exercise training on cognitive function and cortical vascularity in monkeys', *Neuroscience*, June, 1249–48

9   Ansell, E.B. et al. (2012) 'Cumulative adversity and smaller gray matter volume in medial prefrontal, anterior cingulate, and insula regions', *Biological Psychiatry*, July, 57–64

10 Heffernan, T. et al. (2016) 'The impact of active and passive smoking upon health and neurocognitive function', *Frontiers Media* [doi.org/10.3389/978-2-88919-977-8]

11 Sabia, S. et al. (2014) 'Alcohol consumption and cognitive decline in early old age', *Neurology*, January, 332–39

12 Wimber, M. et al. (2015) 'Retrieval induces adaptive forgetting of competing memories via cortical pattern suppression', *Nature Neuroscience*, February, 582–89

13 Weinreich, H. et al. (2006) 'Off the beaten tracks: exploring three aspects of Web navigation', *Proceedings of the 15th International Conference on the World Wide Web*, Edinburgh, 133–42

14 Carr, N. (2011) *The Shallows: How the Internet is Changing the Way We Think, Read and Remember*. New York: Norton and Company Inc.

15 Greenfield, P.M. (2009) 'Technology and informal education: what is taught, what is learned', *Science*, January, 69–71

16 McKinlay, R. (2016) 'Technology: use or lose our navigation skills', *Nature*, March, 573–75

17 Ebbinghaus, E. (1885) *Memory: A Contribution to Experimental Psychology*. Translated by H.A. Ruger and C.E. Bussenius (1913); originally published New York: Teachers College, Columbia University

18 Rapp, D. (2016) 'The consequences of reading inaccurate information', *Current Directions in Psychological Science*, August, 281–85

19 Loftus, E. F. & J.C. Palmer (1974). 'Reconstruction of automobile destruction: an example of the interaction between language and memory', *Journal of Verbal Learning and Verbal Behavior*, October, 585–89

20 National Research Council (2014) *Identifying the Culprit: Assessing Eyewitness Identification*. Washington, D.C.: National Academics Press

21 Wearing, D. (2011) *Forever Today: A Memoir of Love and Amnesia*. London: Transworld Books

22 Finke, C. et al. (2012) 'Preservation of musical memory in an amnesic professional cellist', *Current Biology*, 591–92

'Concentrate all your thoughts upon the work at hand. The sun's rays do not burn until brought to focus.'

Alexander Graham Bell

Scientist, inventor, engineer and innovator (1847–1922)

4: OUR BRAIN AND ATTENTION

We have an excellent capacity to focus and concentrate. From an early age, our instincts direct our attention to what matters to us.

But we now live in a world where there is constant distraction, and our attentional system cannot deal with all the inputs that it receives.

We all need a better understanding of the strengths and limitations of our attentional system so that we can get the best out of it. Distractions interrupt our ability to focus and can even be fatal. We have to learn to pay attention to the right things at the right time.

This chapter provides an explanation of how we pay attention, and why we need to improve our capacity to concentrate.

Part 1: The science explained

How do we pay attention?

A huge amount of information comes in through our eyes. In fact 90% of the information we absorb is visual.

But we do not have the brainpower to deal at a conscious level with all the information we receive. And so we have to filter and select what to pay attention to on a continual basis. We are constantly including and excluding information: we keep information that we are interested in and ignore or delete anything that is anomalous or of no concern to us.

Once we have decided to hold on to information, we then use our store of memories, knowledge and our beliefs to interpret and make sense of it, and then look for further supporting evidence.

Our view of the world therefore affects how we direct our attention and filter new incoming information. We seek and process details that correspond with what we expect, and we reject any evidence that contradicts it.

Our attentional system therefore works like a spotlight.

When we pay attention to something, we shine the spotlight on it. When we need to shift attention, we effectively move the spotlight on to something else, leaving everything else in the dark.

We do not see what we do not expect to see

Whatever falls outside this attentional spotlight is often overlooked, particularly when we are not expecting to see it. We can even miss what is right in front of our nose!

Even when we are concentrating hard, we can still fail to spot signs that would be obvious if we were actually looking for them.

We also lack positive evidence for our lack of attention. In other words, we do not know what we have failed to see, and we only become aware of these misses after they have been pointed out to us.

Attention is therefore a zero-sum game: in order to think about something, we need to stop thinking about something else.

We cannot pay attention to two things at the same time.

How do we know what to focus on?

Our brain's filtering system is known as the *reticular activating system* (RAS), which is a network of neurons and neural fibres running through our brain stem. Nearly all the information entering the brain via our senses is filtered through the RAS. The only sense that goes directly to our emotional centres is our sense of smell.

The RAS is always on, bringing relevant information to our attention.

Figure 4.1: Our reticular activating system

Imagine walking through a busy airport full of noise. Our RAS will respond immediately if our name is called over the public address system. It will help filter out everything else and help us hear only our name above all the other noise.

Our RAS makes sure that we focus on what is important to us.

For example:

» When we buy a new car we start seeing the same car everywhere.

» A pregnant woman will become aware of other pregnant women around her.

» The cry of our baby will wake us up immediately.

» When we are thinking of going on holiday, we will see more travel agents or holiday commercials around us.

Even though the world around us may not alter, our RAS will help us pick out the specific details that we want and need at the time.

Our autopilot makes us lazy thinkers

Conscious thinking requires effort. It uses our brain's cognitive and physical resources. For this reason conscious thinking is a considerably inefficient process.

In order to free up its resources, the brain makes many of our conscious cognitive processes automatic. With practice and repetition, these cognitive processes fall below the level of conscious attention. In other words, we do not need to think about them any more. This is what we call *autopilot*, or *second nature*.

We regularly defer to this autopilot because it feels fast and effortless. And we love being able to repeat familiar patterns of behaviour because they are predictable. As was discussed in Chapter 2, Our Brain and Emotion, Professor Daniel Kahneman calls this fast route to behaviour System 1 thinking.[1]

For example, consider the way that, after years of being a motorist, we no longer have to think about every movement, manoeuvre and signal that we make. We would find it difficult to describe every single thing we do when we drive, especially along a familiar route.

With practice, our automatic performance in any task becomes more efficient until it becomes hard-wired into the physical structure of our brain. This is how habits are formed: a new task demands mental exertion, but as we practise over time, the mental activity that is needed decreases. This is known as *cognitive ease*.

But while automatic processes free our brain up to take on new and additional challenges, they can also be problematic.

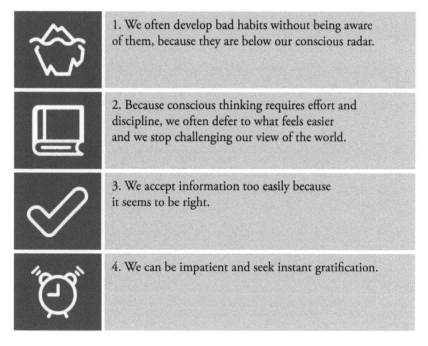

	1. We often develop bad habits without being aware of them, because they are below our conscious radar.
	2. Because conscious thinking requires effort and discipline, we often defer to what feels easier and we stop challenging our view of the world.
	3. We accept information too easily because it seems to be right.
	4. We can be impatient and seek instant gratification.

Figure 4.2: The pitfalls of automatic processes

In order to challenge or override something that we have made automatic in our brain, we effectively need to rewire our brain with a new habit. We can find this very difficult, which is why we may resist change, or taking on something new or different: it all feels like too much hard work. This is discussed in more detail in Chapter 9, Our Brain and Change.

Part 2: Impact on our daily life

Why do experts miss what is right in front of them?

Experts can perform certain tasks effortlessly. When we become an expert at anything, our brain adapts and changes to reflect that expertise.

But expertise can come at a cost. It involves a trade-off in our brain: as we strengthen certain connections, we may weaken others.

An experiment was conducted recently by Dr Trafton Drew at Harvard Medical School with 24 expert radiologists.[2] These radiologists were asked to look at computerised axial tomography (CAT) chest scans and search only for any cancerous nodules or abnormalities that could identify lung cancer. Without their knowledge, in the last scan Dr Drew inserted an image of a gorilla 48 times larger than the average nodule, circled in the picture overleaf.

Over 80% of the radiologists claimed that they had not seen the gorilla, even though an eye-tracking monitor showed that half the group who said they did not see the gorilla had looked straight at it.

➤

Dr Drew commented:

'Part of the reason that radiologists are so good at what they do is that they are very good at narrowly focusing their attention on these lung nodules. And the cost of that is that they're subject to missing other things, even really obvious large things like a gorilla.'

Credit: Dr Trafton Drew, *Psychological Science*, 2013

And so, when we specialise in a particular area of knowledge, we reduce our field of focus and centre only on this domain. In doing so, we tend not to incorporate information outside this specialism. In other words, our attentional spotlight narrows down our perspective and our view becomes increasingly concentrated and constricted.

When our attention is diverted and we do not notice the appearance of an object that is unexpected, it is known as *inattentional blindness*.

Dr Drew's study has important implications for the way we are given instructions, or where we choose to focus our attention: we will tend to see only what we are told or expect to see, and we may miss something else.

Focus is critical to improvement . . .

Our brain's connections strengthen when we decide to pay attention to something. When we practise a technique or a habit every day, we reshape our brain. This applies to whatever we choose to focus on: the more we do it, the more our brain adapts to help us.

. . . but focus can also make us blind

Another aspect of our attentional system, which is closely linked to inattentional blindness, is a phenomenon called *change blindness*, which happens when we fail to spot unexpected changes in our visual world. Once these changes are pointed out or subsequently noticed, they seem obvious.

Professors Christopher Chabris and Daniel Simons have conducted one of the most well-known studies in psychology.[3] Participants were asked to watch a short video in which six people (three in white shirts and three in black shirts) pass basketballs around, and then count the number of passes made by the people in white shirts.

During the game, a 'gorilla' strolls into the middle of the game and beats its chest. Over half the people watching the video fail to see the gorilla, even though it is in full view for several seconds.

In fact, participants were astounded when, having been told about the gorilla, they looked again at the video and saw it!

In 2004, as a result of this and other experiments, the two professors shared the Ig Nobel Prize in Psychology, awarded for 'achievements that first make people laugh, and then make them think'.

Our susceptibility to change blindness is why magicians are so successful. When magicians distract our attention in one direction, we miss what they are doing elsewhere.

During change blindness, the visual system is working and processing inputs as normal, but because there are often too many inputs, a bottleneck occurs in our brain, and we miss what should appear to be obvious once we know it is there.

Change blindness provides an explanation of why...

 Traffic accidents happen.

 Continuity errors in movies go unnoticed.

 Eyewitness testimony is often considered unreliable.

 Drivers looking for other cars on the road may not be aware of cyclists or motorcyclists.

 Baggage screeners at airports find it easier to focus on looking just for single items, such as explosives or knives, rather than trying to detect many items at once.

Figure 4.3: Consequences of change blindness

No one can multitask – not even women!

Many women believe they can multitask, perhaps because of their ability to shift more easily between brain hemispheres than men, as explained in Chapter 1, Our Brain.

However, none of us truly have the ability to multitask. We do not have the brainpower to pay attention to two things at the same time. Imagine, for example, trying to read a book whilst writing a letter!

We may be able to process information from at least two non-competing stimuli at the same time. So we can look at someone, listen and nod our head. Or we can wash the dishes and listen to music.

Figure 4.4: Multitasking – a physiological and psychological impossibility

But trying to use the same cognitive processes together is a physiological impossibility. For example, if we try to count numbers and say the alphabet simultaneously, we quickly realise that it is unfeasible.

Trying to multitask effectively splits our brain. When we quickly withdraw our attention from one task to focus on another, the brain is effectively blank for a split second. This is called a *post-refractory pause* and, over time, the sum of these small losses of attention may be dramatic.

Even one moment of inattention can have significant consequences.

Trying to multitask hurts our brain

Since the 1980s, scientists have been repeating that performance suffers when people try to multitask. We are prone to more errors, we have difficulty retaining information, our focus is impaired and we become more stressed.

In fact, people who try to multitask regularly are much worse at filtering irrelevant information and cannot even switch between tasks, compared to those who tackle one thing at a time.[4]

But we live in a world where our cognitive resources are under constant pressure. According to a report by the McKinsey Global Institute, we spend an average of 13 hours a week dealing with emails.[5] And the more quickly we answer our emails, especially when they pop up when we are in the middle of doing something else, the more productive we feel.

But this constant shifting between tasks is stressful and mentally exhausting. It also increases production of the stress hormone cortisol, which in the long term can even shrink our brain, as discussed further in Chapter 10, Our Brain and Stress.

Why does trying to multitask make us feel so good?

However, while trying to multitask actually makes us less productive, it makes us feel good![6] This may explain why we still try to do it even though it affects our performance. When we feel that we are achieving a great deal – even though we may not actually be as efficient as we would like to think we are – it gives us a sense of emotional fulfilment.

The thrill of our email inbox or Facebook page releases *dopamine*, the neurotransmitter mentioned in Chapter 1, Our Brain. Dopamine helps to regulate our movement, direct our attention and activate the reward centres in our brain.

Dopamine is released in a region of the brain known as the *nucleus accumbens* which registers pleasure. Recreational drugs and alcohol bring about a particularly intense surge of dopamine in this region. And because dopamine also plays a role in learning and memory, it ensures that the brain not only likes something but also stores it as a pleasurable experience in our memory.

When we repeat a behaviour that makes us happy, the nucleus accumbens and the *prefrontal cortex* (the area of the brain involved in attention, planning and execution) work together to make us seek it even more. This is what we call *addiction*.

Our world of constant distraction is feeding a neural addiction in our brain. The more we try to multitask, the more we want to multitask, despite the fact that we are not being as effective as we think. We may feel good, but we are also paying a cognitive price.

Scientists are now claiming that over half the developed world is addicted to something, and in particular this addiction is to technology-driven behaviours, a subject that is explored in Adam Alter's book *Irresistible*.[7] Alter cites stories and examples of how games are crafted to entice and entertain, how a near-win holds more appeal than an actual victory, and how gamers will spend more time on a mission to kill rather than save a life. And, ironically, the people who are designing these games generally limit their own children's usage of technology.

Why is distraction so dangerous?

 Our addiction to technology and often obsessive checking of our email or social media sites are creating a myriad of problems that range from minor errors to potentially fatal consequences.

When we are distracted, we pay less attention and we are more likely to make mistakes. We need to give our attentional system all the help it needs. Because we cannot predict what we will miss or notice in our visual field, we need to limit any distraction.

But distractions are everywhere.

The use of technology, such as satellite navigation systems or talking on the telephone while driving, steals our attention away from the road, and both activities constitute a potentially hazardous situation.

In some Australian, German and Dutch towns, *in-road* traffic lights for pedestrians approaching a road crossing are now positioned on the ground because people are constantly looking down at their phones.

 We cannot give up the technology to which we have become accustomed, but at the same time we do need to recognise the impact of endless distraction and lack of attention on the way we are now living.

We take mental shortcuts to deal with information

Because we can only process a limited amount of information at once without being overloaded, we take mental shortcuts to speed up our decision-making. These mental shortcuts are known as *heuristics* and they help us act or make decisions with minimal effort.

But while heuristics can give us the illusion that we are thinking quickly and efficiently, they can also introduce errors and bias. By deferring to our heuristics we will often rely on what has worked well in the past. The problem is that past experiences, however successful they were at the time, are not always helpful or appropriate for dealing with future challenges. And we are often unable to see beyond our successes in order to interpret new information accurately. As a result, we may not consider different possibilities or listen to opposing viewpoints. This is explained in more detail in Chapter 7, Our Brain and Biases.

Why do we like our comfort zone?

 We like to operate best in places we know, and we are able to navigate a familiar place with greater efficiency. This is called our *comfort zone*.

As change speeds up and uncertainty looms everywhere, our need for comfort becomes stronger than ever. And since many of us are creatures of habit and routine, we stick to what we know: we follow the same route to work, we have our favourite places to stand, sit and shop, and we even take the same holidays. We know what we like and we like what we know.

Our comfort zone is so comfortable that leaving it can feel uncomfortable – or even painful. And when we try to move into unknown territory we often find ourselves rushing back towards what is familiar. Even certain criminals prefer to operate close to their homes, with serious offences usually being committed between just one and two miles from where the offender lives.

The advantage of our comfort zone is that it helps us to stay calm and it reduces our anxiety, which is a healthy strategy when we are living in a fast-moving and rapidly changing world.

However, personal growth and learning are dependent on our openness to new experiences and challenges. The more we learn to deal with the discomfort of change, the more we will expand our comfort zone and thereby increase our overall resilience.

Part 3: Stories and top tips

Attention-related accidents are on the rise

Reports of road accidents caused by drivers failing to pay attention are on the increase. In the United Kingdom, driver distraction (listening to music, using mobile phones or satellite navigation systems), rather than speed, is now the main cause of road accidents, and groups are lobbying for legislation to address driver concentration.

In the United States, the government now has a website (distraction.gov) to help educate the public about the dangers of distracted driving. One simple example is that sending or receiving a text message will divert a driver's eyes from the road for almost five seconds. If we are driving at 55 miles per hour, in those five seconds we are not looking at the road for the entire length of a football field.

The 2016 tragedy in Newbury – a town in the United Kingdom – when a mother and her three children were killed after a lorry driver crashed into them at 50 miles per hour, was linked to driver distraction. The dashcam footage shows that the driver was so focused on his mobile phone that he did not notice any of the traffic in front of him.

The march of the machine

Human fallibility and susceptibility to error and blindness mean that computers are now starting to replace humans in cognitive tasks. For example, computer search patterns (such as Google Flu Trends and Google Dengue Trends) are now more accurate than doctors' predictions, and algorithms, rather than man-made models, are being used to inform decision-making.

In South Korea, scientists have developed technology on a smartphone that will diagnose diseases such as cancer and diabetes with 100% accuracy.[8] This technology is designed to detect biological signals such as biomolecules via the touchscreen. The hope is that this technology will revolutionise medical diagnoses around the world.

In January 2017, the *Financial Times* announced the April launch of Babylon, an app built by 100 artificial-intelligence researchers based in London, which can provide a medical diagnosis and treatment via a smartphone.

Babylon is a repository of amassed data and will be the first robot to be certified clinically by the United Kingdom's Medicines and Healthcare Products Regulatory Agency to provide medical diagnoses – with 92% accuracy, or with ten times more precision than a doctor.

This may be good news for patients. Medical errors and misdiagnoses have been the subject of considerable scrutiny in recent years. Medical leaders across the world are voicing their concerns about the state of healthcare and mounting pressures on doctors, both of which lead to flawed thought processes. About 1,000 people a month in the United

Kingdom die through medical error; this is also reported as being the third-leading cause of death in the United States.[9]

Haematologist-oncologist Jerome Groopman has detailed in the first book of its kind how doctors miss vital signs when making diagnoses.[10] Dr Groopman explains how physicians frequently make snap judgements within as little as 18 seconds about a patient's illness and course of treatment. In order to compensate for their inability to see all the vital signs and symptoms that they need to see, medical professionals are increasingly using a thorough checklist system.

But checklists may not be able to stop the march of technology and the shifting confidence of those patients who may be more reassured by mechanical accuracy than by the human touch with all of its foibles.

The relationship between attention and learning

When we learn to pay attention to detail, we increase our intelligence and accuracy in performing tasks. We also build stronger relationships with other people because we are better able to detect common interests and opportunities for collaboration.

Some schools in the United Kingdom have now banned mobile phones altogether. In 2015, a study published by the London School of Economics found an improvement in exam results among pupils in schools that had banned mobile phones.[11] The researchers cited that the reduced distraction caused by the removal of phones led to better results and increased productivity.

One school in England has recently brought about a complete change in pupils' behaviour since banning mobile phones. Pupils are forbidden to use their phones during the day, with detentions imposed on anyone found with a handset between 8:15am and 5:45pm. These rules are supported by the pupils' parents.

The head teacher who is behind this initiative claims that the removal of this distraction has meant that more time is spent conversing and debating with each other, instead of spending time worrying about social media. The school still uses tablets and laptops for teaching, but pupils themselves have said that the experience has freed them from the pressures of social media, leaving them better able to concentrate on their studies and on building relationships with each other.

We all need to pay attention. As the author and Zen teacher Ezra Bayda says:

'When you really pay attention, everyone is your teacher.'

Acknowledge that you cannot multitask, particularly in a situation that could jeopardise your safety. Remember that a car is potentially a lethal weapon! A few seconds of inattention could have permanent and deadly consequences. Focus on one thing at a time.

Work at changing your routine and leaving your comfort zone on a regular basis. Learn something new, such as a new language, musical instrument or sport. People who regularly seek out fresh experiences tend to be more creative and emotionally resilient than those who remain stuck in their comfort zone.

Accept challenges to your thinking. Question the heuristics or mental shortcuts that you are using. Even if you have an expertise or specialism, you may not have all the right answers. Welcome other viewpoints, even if they contradict what you think you know.

Remove all possible distractions in meetings. Computers and telephones should be kept out of sight so that you are able to concentrate fully on what people are saying. You will take in far more information about people if you pay full attention to them.

Expand your view of the world. Learn to look around you and take the time to pick up details about your environment and other people. Think about everything you are taking in through your senses.

References for Chapter 4

1 Kahneman, D. (2012) *Thinking Fast and Slow*. London: Penguin Books

2 Drew, G. et al. (2013) 'The invisible gorilla strikes again: sustained inattentional blindness in expert observers', *Psychological Science*, July, 1848–53

3 Chabris, C. & D. Simons (2011) *The Invisible Gorilla: And Other Ways Our Intuition Deceives Us*. New York: HarperCollins

4 Ophir, E. et al. (2009) 'Cognitive control in media multitaskers', *Proceedings of the National Academy of Sciences*, 15583–87

5 Chui, M. et al. (2012) 'The social economy: unlocking value and productivity', McKinsey Global Institute, July [www.mckinsey.com]

6 Wang, Z. & J.M. Tchernev (2012) 'The "myth" of media multitasking: reciprocal dynamics of media multitasking, personal needs, and gratifications', *Journal of Communication*, April, 493–513

7 Alter, A. (2017) *Irresistible: The Rise of Addictive Technology and the Business of Keeping Us Hooked*. New York: Bodley Head

8 Yeon W. et al. (2011) 'A touchscreen as a biomolecule detection platform', *Angewandte Chemie International Edition*, November, 748–51

9 Makary, M.A. & M. Daniel (2016) 'Medical error – the third leading cause of death in the US', *BMJ*, May [doi.org/10.1136/bmji2139]

10 Groopman, J. (2007) *How Doctors Think*. New York: Houghton Mifflin Company

11 Beland, L-P. & R. Murphy (2015) 'Communication: technology, distraction & student performance', *Centre for Economic Performance*, May, 61–76

'Without language one cannot talk to people and understand them; one cannot understand their hopes and aspirations, grasp their history, appreciate their poetry or savour their songs.'

Nelson Mandela

Anti-apartheid revolutionary, politician and philanthropist (1918–2013)

5: OUR BRAIN AND LANGUAGE

About this chapter

Language is one of our most significant evolutionary adaptations. Our ability to communicate using language is fundamental to our success as humans. Through our use of words, nuance and tonality, we are able to convey different meanings and levels of intensity in a way that is not possible for animals.

For the last 150 years, scientists have been studying the way we formulate and interpret language. Our extensive linguistic ability has enabled us to develop ideas, transform societies and incite others to action.

This chapter looks at language – both written and spoken – and how it works in our brain. Research is continuing in this area and there is much about our language systems and pathways that we are still discovering today.

Part 1: The science explained

Where is language processed in our brain?

When we hear a word, our brain determines whether it recognises the word and its meaning. Scientists have used brain imaging to localise where in the brain we hear sounds and then where we process language.

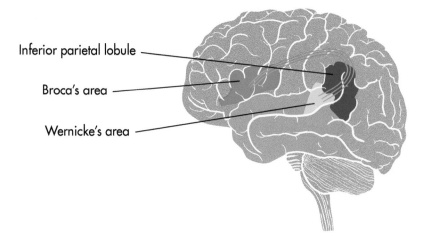

Inferior parietal lobule

Broca's area

Wernicke's area

Figure 5.1: Our language pathways

Three scientists in particular provided our first significant insights into how we process language:

1) Paul Broca

In 1861, Paul Broca, a French neurologist, discovered a region of the brain associated with the production of spoken language. He found that damage to this area resulted in speech deficiencies.

Broca had been working with a patient known as 'Tan' because this was the only syllable the patient could utter. After Tan died, Broca conducted a post-mortem and found damage to an area of Tan's brain associated with speech production.

This area is now referred to as *Broca's area* and it is where we *construct* language.

Broca's work in the world of brain science and understanding was pioneering. Since then, research into brain problems has continued to provide valuable insights into how language works in our brain.

2) Carl Wernicke

Ten years after Broca, German neurologist Carl Wernicke found that damage to Broca's area was not the only place in the brain where a language deficit could occur.

Wernicke identified a language problem in which certain patients were able to speak but were not able to comprehend language. By examining the brains of patients suffering from this language problem, Wernicke revealed damage at a junction of the parietal, temporal and occipital lobes. This region of the brain is now known as *Wernicke's area* and is associated with the *understanding* of spoken and written language.

3) Norman Geschwind

In the 1960s, Norman Geschwind discovered that the *inferior parietal lobule* (IPL) of our brain also plays an important role in processing language. The neurons in the IPL can take stimuli from all our senses (this is called *multi-modal*) and help our brain understand the construction, sound and meaning of spoken and written words.

The IPL is one of the last structures of the human brain to have developed over the course of human evolution and it exists only in a basic form in other primates. The IPL also matures later in children, which may explain why we cannot begin to read and write until we are about five years old.

The legacy of these three scientists is that we are now able to link certain language impairments with specific brain regions, and we can see how brain recovery can result in neural restructuring where brain pathways are repaired.

How is language affected by injury or brain trauma?

 Communication problems after brain injury are very common. A language disorder that affects both production and comprehension of language is known as *aphasia* (or in a less severe form as *dysphasia*).

The most common types of aphasia are shown Figure 5.2. These are only general labels for aphasia because, depending on the areas of the brain affected, and the severity of the injury, people may experience more than one kind of communication problem.

There are many different successful ways of treating aphasia, depending on the type and cause. Speech and language therapy is the main treatment and, over time, this does help to alleviate symptoms.

Global Aphasia	Patients cannot read or write and their speech is very limited, speaking and understanding only a little.
Broca's Aphasia	Patients' ability to express language in the form of speech and writing is severely reduced. They speak mostly in nouns and produce a few words in non-fluent sentences. Example: 'Dog...walk...food...forget.'
Wernicke's Aphasia	Patients may not be able to read or write. They can speak fluently in nonsense without realising that this is happening. Example: 'Train and better teacher football headaches and finishing. Very good London.'
Anomic Aphasia	Patients understand speech and can read, but cannot speak or write easily.

Figure 5.2: Types of aphasia

Language: a left-brained thing?

Scientific evidence suggests that we use both hemispheres of the brain to enable us to communicate.

However, a long-held belief is that our construction and interpretation of language is left-hemisphere dominated.

In most people, it does seem that the left hemisphere is dominant for language, while the right hemisphere is involved in understanding simple words, metaphors, poetic metres and intonation.

But when the left hemisphere is damaged, the right hemisphere will step up and undertake a greater role in processing language. This has been observed in young children who have suffered from epilepsy and who undergo an operation called an *hemispherectomy*, in which a large section of the affected hemisphere is removed. After the left hemisphere has been removed in these cases, the right hemisphere has assumed responsibility for language functions almost perfectly.

The capacity of the right hemisphere to take on many of the main functions of language has important implications for those with damage to their left hemisphere. It also proves that our brain, although bilaterally organised, works as one unit.

Intonation affects meaning

Intonation – the tone of our voice – is one of the methods by which we communicate. Functional magnetic resonance imaging (fMRI) has provided valuable insights into how our brain separates speech into words and intonation.[1]

Most words are interpreted in the left temporal lobe for processing, while the intonation is channelled to the right side of the brain, a region more stimulated by music.

The emotion contained in the speaker's tone can ignite an emotional response in the listener that is remembered long after the actual message has been delivered.

Our intonation affects the meaning of the words we use. Think about the following sentence:

» 'I didn't say he should stroke the dog.'

By emphasising different words through our intonation, we automatically change its meaning.

'*I* didn't say he should stroke the dog.'	Someone else said it.
'I **didn't** say he should stroke the dog.'	I am denying it.
'I didn't *say* he should stroke the dog.'	I implied it, pointed or wrote it down.
'I didn't say *he* should stroke the dog.'	Someone else should stroke the dog.
'I didn't say he **should** stroke the dog.'	It is not an obligation.
'I didn't say he should *stroke* the dog.'	He should just look at the dog.
'I didn't say he should stroke the **dog**.'	I meant that he should stroke the cat.

Different words light up different parts of our brain

 Recent research is providing additional insight into language as a complex set of activities in our brain that may not be localised solely in one or two areas.

A recent study has shown that, for the first time, scientists have been able to map different groups of words to different parts of the brain in order to examine how we represent meaning, or *semantics*.[2]

Using an fMRI scanner to monitor blood flow, scientists asked participants to listen to two hours of storytelling with over 10,000 English words involved. The results showed that our brain groups words together depending on what their significance is to us. For example, the same region in the temporal lobe – associated with emotion – lights up with words such as 'wife', 'house', 'pregnant' and 'family'.

Similarly, illustrative and vivid words that enable our brain to conjure up images (such as 'red rose' or 'blue sky') are reflected in activity in the occipital lobe, the area of the brain associated with processing visual information.

This research is a valuable starting point in explaining how information is stored across our brain. Clinical professionals may be able to use this semantic map to treat language disorders, and we may also gain greater insight into the neurological impact of messages in the public domain.

Our brain is organised for communication

Whether words are spoken or demonstrated with sign language, the brain treats them the same, and the same neural regions are activated by both.[3]

Our brain interprets signing as language and not as gestures that would be associated more with games such as charades. In fact, research shows that signing and charades activate different brain areas, even when some of the hand gestures are similar.

Researchers showed 29 deaf signers using American Sign Language (ASL) and 64 hearing native-English speakers pictures of objects such as a cup or a parrot and asked the subjects to either sign or speak the word.

At the same time they measured brain activity and blood flow using a positron emission tomography (PET) scanner.

In both groups Broca's and Wernicke's areas were equally active.

Our brain *sees* words

The brain converts words into visual associations almost immediately.

As explained in Chapter 6, Our Brain and Visual Perception, we have an area in the brain called the *fusiform face area* (FFA) which recognises faces quickly. We also have a *visual word form area* (VWFA) that helps us read words quickly; this helps us see the whole word at once rather than analysing its component parts.[4]

When we are skilled at reading, we do not need to process the sounds in each letter. Instead our brain recognises words quickly as part of a pattern.

In 2013, Taiwanese-born entrepreneur ShaoLan Hsueh gave a TED talk on how to read Chinese. The following year she published a book entitled *Chineasy: The New Way to Read Chinese.*[5]

Motivated to teach her English-speaking children to read Mandarin, ShaoLan's aim was to create a pictorial connection to Chinese words through their associated images.

Armed with her understanding of Chinese characters (she is the daughter of a calligrapher), ShaoLan commissioned the graphic artist Noma Bar to create a simple and visual system of symbols.

Credit: ShaoLan Hsueh and Thames & Hudson

Part 2: Impact on our daily life

Why nouns make us respond more quickly than verbs

When we learn to read as children, we learn nouns before verbs. We are more able to form a mental image of nouns than of most verbs, which is why nouns tend to be easier to learn. And, as adults, we respond more quickly to nouns than other words.[6]

Advertising often uses adjectives as nouns such as:

'Rightmove. Find your **happy**.'

'Show us your Heinz.
Where there is **happy** there has to be Heinz.'

'Olay. Your best **beautiful**.'

When we use one part of speech as another (a term known as *antimeria*), such as using a verb as a noun, it helps attract more attention and for that reason is a clever advertising ploy.

We see words as shapes

As mentioned earlier in this chapter, our *visual word form area* (VWFA) enables us to read a word as a whole and become familiar with *word shapes*.

This is why road signs are increasingly using upper and lower case together, rather than upper case only, because we can see the pattern of the word, register it quickly and then respond quickly.

Compare this road sign:

to this one:

Understanding how our brain reads words also has important implications for how we teach children to read, particularly those who struggle with traditional methods. For example, children may find it easier to see the whole word as a visual object instead of having to learn it phonetically.

Can an understanding of language help stroke patients?

Strokes often affect people's ability to speak or perceive language. If a stroke has affected the right side of the brain, the patient may be unable to detect emotional intonation, whereas damage to the left side of the brain could affect their ability to comprehend certain words.

Knowledge of how language is processed in the healthy brain may therefore help scientists to develop more effective solutions for stroke patients to regain their mastery of language construction and comprehension.

What do our emails say about us?

Researchers are examining the language we use in emails. Thousands of emails have been analysed from participants who also completed personality questionnaires assessing levels of extrovertism or neurosis.[7] The more neurotic the participants, the greater their use of exclamation and quotation marks and the more erratic their use of commas and adverbs.

We now rely heavily on email for the majority of our communication. As discussed in Chapter 4, Our Brain and Attention, we are spending an average of 13 hours a week sorting out our inbox.[8] We rely heavily on email for most of our communication, even when we would be better served by face-to-face contact.

When we overuse email, we do not promote proper dialogue or problem-solving and, worse, we risk misinterpretation.

In 2001, the chief executive of a US healthcare software-development company, with 3,100 employees worldwide, sent an email to his 400 managers.

This is an excerpt from his email:

'We are getting less than 40 hours of work from a large number of our K.C.-based EMPLOYEES. The parking lot is sparsely used at 8 a.m.; likewise at 5 p.m. As managers you either do not know what your EMPLOYEES are doing; or you do not CARE. In either case, you have a problem and you will fix it or I will replace you. NEVER in my career have I allowed a team which worked for me to think they had a 40-hour job. I have allowed YOU to create a culture which is permitting this. NO LONGER.

I am tabling the promotions until I am convinced that the ones being promoted are the solution, not the problem. If you are the problem, pack your bags.

I think this parental type action SUCKS. However, what you are doing, as managers, with this company makes me SICK. It makes me sick to have to write this directive.

I am giving you two weeks to fix this. My measurement will be the parking lot: it should be substantially full at 7:30 AM and 6:30 PM. The pizza man should show up at 7:30 PM to feed the starving teams working late. The lot should be half full on Saturday mornings. We have a lot of work to do. If you do not have enough to keep your teams busy, let me know immediately.

You have the responsibility for our EMPLOYEES. I will hold you accountable. You have allowed this to get to this state. You have two weeks. Tick, tock.'

This email was posted on Yahoo, and in three days the valuation of the company, which had been $1.5 billion on 20 March, plummeted by 22%.

An analyst with Goldman Sachs was reported as saying:

'It did raise two real questions for investors. One: Has anything potentially changed at [the company] to cause such a seemingly violent reaction? And two: Is this a CEO that investors are comfortable with?'

The power of words

The language we use has a powerful effect on our brain. A Spanish study has shown how the brain's region for taste and smell (*olfactory cortex*) lit up when shown the words 'garlic', 'cinnamon' and 'jasmine'.[9] Words can therefore stimulate our brain to conjure up a real sensory experience.

Another study in France used words describing motions such as 'grasp' and 'kick' and observed an increase in activity in the motor cortex, which coordinates the body's movements.[10] More specifically, when the movement was arm-related (such as 'grasp'), one area of the motor cortex responded, and when the movement concerned the leg (such as 'kick'), a different part was triggered.

It therefore seems that our brain cannot tell the difference between reading an experience and actually living through it; the brain behaves in exactly the same way in both cases.

OUR NAME

Our attentional system switches on when we hear what is relevant to us. And we love the sound of our name being used.

Hearing our name validates us and affirms our identity. As Dale Carnegie said:

'Remember that a person's name is to that person the sweetest and most important sound in any language.'

INSTANT

Some words actually spur us on to buy. If we read or hear 'instant', 'immediate' and 'fast', our brain's reward centre is activated. We now live in a world of instant gratification and we have become used to getting real-time information and feedback. For example, we can see and upload photographs as soon as we have taken them, and then gauge people's responses immediately. When we cannot have something we want quickly we become impatient and anxious.

And so, when we use language that denotes speed and immediacy in our conversations with others, we reduce any uncertainty that they may feel and we activate their brain's reward circuit.

NEW

Our brain loves being stimulated, and nothing stimulates it more than novelty. For this reason, we love being told what is 'new'.

But we have to strike the right balance between novelty and familiarity. Our impulse for having what is new drives most industries today, and the language of novelty often constitutes the sales message. As Steve Jobs famously said (talking about Apple products):

'A lot of times people don't know what they want until you show it to them.'

But we still like familiarity because it feels safe and secure. When something represents a significant departure from the old, it can represent too much of a challenge. So even though we have a strong novelty bias, we also like to be reassured and reminded of what we are used to.

BECAUSE

The word 'because' is powerful since our brain just needs a reason – and often any reason will do! The word 'because' informs us and helps us to make connections in our brain.

> You need this product **because** . . .

> We always use this product **because** . . .

> I like this one better than that one **because** . . .

We are more likely to accept unpopular or unfavourable decisions when we are given a reason. We often just need to know *why*. We only have to imagine how we feel when we are sitting on a train and it suddenly stops for no apparent reason. Our anxiety levels build, the longer we are left waiting for an explanation.

YOU/YOUR

When we combine 'you'/'your' with 'because', the effect is very powerful.

> Buy this product today **because** it will really help **your** business.

Go and buy a big car **because your** family is growing.

Do you want to know why **you** are always late?
It's **because you** need a new watch.

TOGETHER

Because we need to belong to a social group, the word 'together' carries a great deal of weight. So when we hear 'together', our brain's reward centre is activated and we feel more positive about what we are doing.

A recent study examined the impact of the word 'together' on the work of two groups.[11] Both groups started a task together and were then divided to work separately.

Group 1 were told that they were working on the task 'together', even though they had now been allocated a separate room.

Group 2 were just given the task.

The results showed that Group 1 worked for 48% longer, solved more problems correctly and enjoyed the work more than Group 2.

The word 'together' made all the difference.

The danger with NO . . .

Because we are naturally programmed to be negative and look for threats to our survival, we are easily influenced by words that sound negative.

Our brain responds in the same way, both when we express negative words ourselves and when we spend time with people who constantly use negative language.

Brain imaging studies have shown that if we see the word 'no', even for just a second, the same hormones and neurotransmitters that are produced in stressful situations are immediately released. These chemical releases interrupt our normal brain function, affecting the way that we think and communicate.

And it is not just the word 'no'. Any words with a negative association will have a harmful impact on us and can worsen our symptoms if we are feeling depressed or anxious. This has important implications for doctors and dentists, who may say 'This won't hurt much' or 'I have some bad news'. Our brain is then psychologically ready and primed for experiencing pain.

The research of Baruch Krauss, Associate Professor of Paediatrics at Harvard Medical School, focuses on anxiety and pain relief in children undergoing medical procedures. Professor Krauss uses language with children that engages them and diverts their attention away from the pain and towards a motor activity such as colouring. He also examines the way children later recall and speak about their experience. By encouraging children to concentrate on a fun task, he finds that this is what they remember from the experience.

. . . and the importance of YES

It is not easy or straightforward to convert the brain from a negative to a positive state using just positive words. When we have been influenced negatively, we then have to work much harder to generate positive thoughts. In other words, negative information has a more profoundly lasting effect on us and is *cognitively stickier* than positive information.[12] We observe this phenomenon when consumer confidence, eroded by an economic downturn, remains resistant to emergent signals of recovery.

Positive words and thoughts stimulate the motivational centres of the brain into action and they make us more resilient to challenges. Our brain needs a constant diet of positive language and emotion if it is to build durable personal resources and coping mechanisms.[13] By generating positive language about ourselves and others, we decrease the impact of negative emotions and actively lay the cornerstone for a healthy, happy brain.

When to use BUT

The use of the word 'but' can kill communication and the flow of ideas and suggestions. We often start a sentence with it and we do not even realise how much we use it! The problem with the word 'but' is that it is a negation word: it cancels everything that precedes it:

'I appreciate what you are saying, *but* . . .'

'That is a great proposal, *but* . . .'

'You have done a great job, *but* . . .'

When we hear 'but', we forget or ignore anything that has been said before it, even if the preceding words have been positive. We sometimes try to reduce the impact of 'but' by using 'however' – which is just a longer way of saying 'but'!

Some people are even advised to say the word 'and' instead of 'but'. This does not work either because 'and' is often still heard as a 'but', particularly if it is used too much. The way that we often arrange our sentences in two halves – a positive, followed by a negative statement – means that our brain is still hooking on to the negative.

However, 'but' can be used in a positive way. Because 'but' effectively invalidates what goes before, it can be used as a refocusing technique. For example, when we need to deliver bad news, we can apply 'but' to soften the blow, particularly when used in conjunction with the word 'because':

'We cannot do this **because** . . . ,

. . . **but** what we can do is . . .'

Here *but* is used to minimise the preceding negative and to emphasise the positive alternative.

Be careful of DON'T

Although many words we use are *seen* by our brain, the word 'don't' is not one of them! We say to people:

'**Don't** look behind you.'

'I **don't** want you to be upset about this.'

'Please **don't** hesitate to contact me.'

We say to small children:

> **'Don't** touch that.'

> **'Don't** knock that over.'

> **'Don't** spill that drink.'

And then we are surprised when we witness the very behaviour we think we have tried to prevent!

When we are told not to think about something, our brain immediately conjures up the very image or behaviour associated with the word that we can see. If we would like people to do something for us, we therefore need to reinforce what we *want* to see, and not what we *do not* want to see!

Why do some words really annoy and even repel us?

There are some words and phrases that we all find annoying. Lucy Kellaway, the former *Financial Times* journalist, presents annual *corporate guff awards* for terrible use of language in business. These include such terms as 'chief manifesto specialist', 'life-performance solutions', 'through the lens of humanity', 'right culture' and 'values-driven organisation'. Kellaway's dictionary of business jargon, or *guffipedia*, contains an extensive list of words and phrases that many of us will be familiar with!

These *guff* words of corporate nonsense mostly make us feel irritated and prompt us to switch off: our brain does not appreciate the simple made complex.

There are also some words that actually make us shudder, and even evoke an extreme visceral response, when we hear them. This phenomenon is known as *word aversion*.

Professor Mark Lieberman at the University of Pennsylvania explains that our aversive reaction to these words is not based on misuse, overuse or grammatical error. Our distaste is based on the fact that these words actually feel disgusting. Among the words that Professor Lieberman lists as causing offence are 'cornucopia', 'hardscrabble', 'pugilist' and 'wedge'. Other words that provoke a negative reaction are 'crevice', 'slacks', 'luggage' and 'phlegm'.

But it seems that the most repellent word of all is 'moist'.[14] Understanding word aversion may help us guard against the words that we should not under any circumstances use in promotional or marketing literature.

Neuroscientist Dr David Eagleman suggests that the word-aversion phenomenon may be similar to *synaesthesia*, where our senses conjoin and certain sounds or words are associated with images or emotions.

This subject is covered in more detail in Chapter 8, Our Brain and Creativity.

The problem with the feedback sandwich

Many businesses follow a well-trodden path for performance appraisal every year whereby managers give feedback to their employees. The format that is most frequently used for this process is called the *feedback sandwich*.

Sadly, the feedback sandwich is still being taught in communication and development initiatives today. While the intention behind it is generally well meaning, its effect is often negative.

So how we do we make a feedback sandwich?

The bread on the outside of the sandwich constitutes positive or neutral feedback. The filling in the middle is composed of advice for further development; this filling is often heard as the negative or main message.

The problem with the feedback sandwich is that our brain's natural negativity bias interferes with the whole process. The *positive* messages on both sides of the *development* segment are filtered out and the developmental *filling* is quickly turned into criticism. A feeling of being censured or even attacked is therefore what the employee is left with.

A feedback sandwich looks something like this:

'John, I think you have worked really hard this year. Well done for meeting your objectives.

In terms of your development I have heard that some of your colleagues find you quite difficult. So we will need to think about how we can address that. Perhaps there are some training courses you can attend.

But overall you have won us a great deal of new business and well done for that.'

We are now so conditioned by the traditional appraisal discussion that, when we hear the positive words, we brace ourselves for what is coming next!

Rather than motivate employees to do a better job, the feedback sandwich often deters and even crushes effort. The process is worsened by the fact that appraisal discussions often take place only on an annual basis, so managers effectively avoid difficult discussions throughout the year and then open the floodgates, expecting employees to cope with a tsunami of comments all at once.

In order for feedback to do a good job, it needs to be given regularly and often. The praise and criticisms messages that make up the feedback sandwich should be separated to avoid confusing or demoralising an employee. The feedback sandwich as one standalone process that combines both positive and negative messages simply does not work.

Three separate feedback conversations

1) Give praise – and be specific

Praise should be used to acknowledge good effort or successful achievement. This should happen every time the employee does something praiseworthy, not reserved for a formal setting or an annual review. When we give praise immediately after an event, we are more likely to see that behaviour or action being repeated and reinforced in the future. It is important to remember that praise must be specific.

Teachers could say to their pupils:

» 'Your story is very good. I particularly like the way you gave real examples and brought it to life.'

Managers could say to their employees:

» 'You have worked really hard on this project. I especially appreciated how you coached the new team members and worked closely with them to bring them up to speed.'

2) Help someone to improve – and focus on the future, not the past

When we are in a position whereby we can influence someone else's performance of a task, we need to consider how to structure our support of their efforts. Any conversation must be carefully timed so that the person can direct their attention on future endeavour. For example, if we are trying to encourage someone to be better at giving presentations – and in particular, organising visual information – we need to tell them what they should be doing *just before* their next presentation. In a sense, we are feeding *forward*, not *back*.

This conversation could sound like:

» 'Sarah, I know you are preparing for the meeting next Tuesday. I have a few suggestions that may help with the way you set out your points and illustrations. Shall we go through them together on Monday?'

Because the conversation is directing effort towards a future activity, the person on the receiving end does not feel criticised but rather can focus on improvement. This is much more effective than telling them what they did not do well just after an event, which can often be demotivating.

3) Change an aspect of their behaviour – and be clear and factual

When we are asking someone to change an aspect of how they behave, we need to be calm, clear, factual and specific. Generalisations such as 'You always do this' or 'You never do that' are not helpful and simply result in the other person becoming defensive. We need to refer to the exact action or behaviour and when it happened. It is also important that the person acknowledges what has happened before you proceed with the conversation.

» 'Peter, I noticed you interrupted Sam three times at last Tuesday's meeting. What was your reason for this?'

The explanation that is then given by Peter also serves as an acceptance that this situation occurred.

We should then explain the impact of that particular act or behaviour:

» 'Because you interrupted him he was unable to give us a full briefing. As a result we need more time to go through it all together again.'

The impact can be attached to the leader, the team or even the business. It is then important to ask them to help us find a solution or way forward:

» 'How do you suggest we handle the next meeting?'

and then agree a new action together.

» 'So what we will do is . . .'

The difference between this approach and the feedback sandwich is that the messages are not mixed and the conversation here is focused on one incident and one specific outcome. The person is left with a clear message about what needs to happen next, rather than feeling personally attacked by mass generalisations.

Importantly, when this approach is used to address small incidents or episodes at the time when they occur, it reduces the need for a bigger discussion, which many managers avoid anyway.

Part 3: Stories and top tips

Language inspires us

We are all aware of the inspiring effect of words. Throughout history, words have been used to mobilise and ignite nations.

As mentioned in Chapter 2, Our Brain and Emotion, even years later, we can quote Martin Luther King's 'I have a dream'. And we can still appreciate Winston Churchill's 'This was their finest hour'.

Throughout history, words have communicated aspiration, hope, change and endeavour; they have reflected and reinforced belief, and unified people behind them.

Today, we can see how politicians and their aides use language to reach the masses. For example, Frank Luntz, a political consultant in the United States, understands the power of language and has advised Republicans for years on their messaging strategy. In the 1990s, Luntz suggested the reframing of 'global warming' to 'climate change' because it sounded less frightening.

In a party memo (reported in 2003) Luntz stated:

'A compelling story, even if factually inaccurate, can be more emotionally compelling than a dry recitation of the truth.'

As Chapter 2, Our Brain and Emotion, has already explained, when emotion is injected into our language it can radically mobilise mass effort. This can be seen clearly in Donald Trump's use of language in the run-up to the 2016 US presidential election:

Television interview with Jimmy Kimmel, December 2015

'But, Jimmy, the problem – I mean, *look*, I'm for it. But *look*, we have people coming into our country that are *looking* to do tremendous harm. You *look* at the two – **look** at Paris. *Look* at what happened in Paris. I mean, these people, they did not come from Sweden, okay? *Look* at what happened in Paris. *Look* at what happened last week in California, with, you know, 14 people dead. Other people going to die, they're so badly injured. And what I wanna do is find out what it – you know, you can't solve a problem until you find out what's the root cause. And I wanna find out, what is the problem, what's going on.'

Trump's language is not complex and his sentences are short and impactful. He draws people in ('Look') and he uses simple techniques such as repetition and exaggeration. The net effect is that people are swept along on a wave of rhetoric.

Similar techniques can be observed in Trump's inauguration speech, which at 15 minutes was also one of the shortest in history. His opening was punchy and explicit:

'We will face challenges. We will confront hardships, but we will get the job done.'

Trump's words then painted a dark and depressing picture of a United States filled with gangs, drugs, crime, poverty and unemployment, and featuring graphic allusions to 'rusted-out factories scattered like tombstones' and 'American carnage'.

Donald Trump's language throughout was unconventional, evocative and dramatic, stirring strong emotions and polarising people all over the world.

Language sells

As Chapter 7, Our Brain and Biases, will explain in more detail, language can have a powerful influencing effect on our behaviour. Advertising plays to this and often uses emotional messaging to sell the benefits of products or services. For example, an explanation of how a car will improve our lifestyle is a more successful sales message than a list of the various features of that car.

Emotional statements sell. We only have to consider Harley-Davidson's sales message:

'What we sell is the ability for a 43-year-old accountant to dress in black leather, ride through small towns and have people be afraid of him.'

Advertisers understand the power of language and the words that will get people to buy. Apple's language appeals cleverly to two demographics at opposing ends of the technology spectrum: bookworms and digital natives.

> ### 'MacBook. The most interesting book in the world.'

Promotional messages avoid the language of price and expense, which are negatively loaded, and focus instead on adventure and lifestyle:

> ### 'The new Mercedes SLK is as wild as you want it to be. With a retractable hard top, a 302 hp supercharged engine and undeniable style, the SLK will take you anywhere you go.'

Language is therefore used to sell products, reposition brands and influence our behaviour in ways that we often do not realise or question.

As will be explained in Chapter 7, Our Brain and Biases, the framing effect is potent.

» We are more likely to buy meat that is 90% lean than 10% fat; £50 a month sounds much more manageable than £600 a year.

» We are susceptible to language that helps us avoid a loss rather than make a gain, such as:

> '**You are losing** money by not replacing the boiler in your home.'

> versus:

> '**You will save** money by replacing the boiler in your home.'

» We like feeling that we have found a good deal, which is why Buy One Get One Free (BOGOF) offers are highly effective. These deals are so seductive that we often end up buying what we do not need or did not even want in the first place!

Stories turn on our brain

Stories engage us and fascinate us. They inspire us and give us hope. Through stories, we connect with people and identify with their challenges and struggles. And, more importantly, we remember them.

Studies on the neurobiology of storytelling have considered the impact of personal stories on brain function. When we hear a story, the same area of the brain lights up as if we were actually telling the story ourselves.[15]

We remember stories over statistics. Professor Jennifer Aake, at Stanford's Graduate School of Business, refers to a study in which students were asked to give a one-minute presentation to their fellow students.

Only one of the presentations contained a story, while all the other presentations included statistics.

The researcher then asked the students to note down on paper what they remembered.

5% of the students remembered a statistic.

63% of the students remembered the story.

When we hear stories that engage us emotionally, we produce more *oxytocin*, the neurotransmitter released when we build trust or invest in loving relationships.[16] The effect of this is that our memories of these stories are more enduring.

The influence of storytelling on the creative arts such as writing and movie-making may be observed in Joseph Campbell's *The Hero with a Thousand Faces*.[17] Campbell's work details how all storytelling is largely built around the principles of the *hero myth*, with which we all engage. The hero, sometimes reluctantly, accepts a mission, overcomes adversity and in the end succeeds. This theme runs through many of the movies and stories that we enjoy today.

Nelson Mandela was born in 1918 in South Africa. He joined the African National Congress, working against the ruling National Party's apartheid policies.

In 1962 he was brought to trial on the basis of trying to overthrow the government. He was sentenced to life in prison.

In 1990 Mandela was released from prison and restarted his work to end apartheid. In 1993 he was awarded the Nobel Peace Prize and in 1994 he became the first black president of South Africa.

Nelson Mandela overcame hardship and fought for what he believed in. He became an inspirational role model all over the world. His story will be told for years to come.

As Mandela said:

'I learned that courage was not the absence of fear, but the triumph over it. The brave man is not he who does not feel afraid, but he who conquers that fear.'

Simplify your language and make it visual and memorable. Avoid jargon where possible. Think about the people you are talking to and be aware that the language of your business or specialism may not mean much to others. Use words that the brain can digest easily and visualise quickly.

Practise reframing your messages in order to make them more effective. Think carefully about your words, the context in which you are positioning them and where you are putting particular emphasis. Be aware of the impact of your language on other people. Our words have the ability to create or destroy in seconds.

Engage people on a personal level by telling a story. We especially love stories that trigger emotional responses. Try to begin your presentations with a personal story to hook your audience. Remember that stories ignite the brain.

Avoid using negatively charged words or words that elicit distaste in others. The strength of word aversion, combined with our natural negativity bias, means that we need to work harder at using positive and supportive language.

Kick-start and stimulate the senses where possible. Sensory words can bring your language to life and engage other people in your message. The more senses you activate in others, the more they will remember your message.

References for Chapter 5

1 Scott, S.K. and R.J. Wise (2003) 'Functional imaging and language: a critical guide to methodology and analysis', *Speech Communication*, August, 7–21

2 Huth, A.G. et al. (2016) 'Natural speech reveals the semantic maps that tile human cerebral cortex', *Nature*, April, 453–58

3 Emmorey, K. et al. (2007) 'The neural correlates of sign versus word production', *Neuroimage*, May, 202–08

4 Glezer, L.S. et al. (2009) 'Evidence for highly selective neuronal tuning to whole words in the "Visual Word Form Area"', *Neuron*, April, 199–204

5 Hsueh, S. (2014) *Chineasy: The New Way to Read Chinese*. London: Thames and Hudson

6 Rodriquez-Fornells, A. et al. (2010) 'Nouns and verbs are learned in different parts of the brain', *Neuroimage*, February, 156 [www.sciencedaily.com/releases/2010/02/100225084640.htm]

7 Oberlander, J. and A. Gill (2004) 'Language generation and personality: two dimensions, two stages, two hemispheres?', *Papers from the AAAI Spring Symposium on Architectures for Modeling Emotion: Cross-Disciplinary Foundations*, Spring, 104–11

8 Chui, M. et al. (2012) 'The social economy: unlocking valueand productivity', McKinsey Global Institute [www.mckinsey.com]

9 Gonzalez. J. et al. (2006) 'Reading cinnamon activates olfactory brain regions', *NeuroImage*, August, 906–12

10 Boulenger, V. et al. (2009) 'Grasping ideas with the motor system: semantic somatotopy in idiom comprehension', *Cerebral Cortex*, August, 1905–14

11 Carr, P. & G. Walton (2014) 'Cues of working together fuel intrinsic motivation', *Journal of Experimental Psychology*, July, 169–84

12 Ledgerwood, A. & A.E. Boydstun (2013) 'Sticky prospects: loss frames are cognitively stickier than gain frames', *Journal of Experimental Psychology*, March, 1–10

13 Garland, E.L. et al. (2010) 'Upward spirals of positive emotions counter downward spirals of negativity: insights from the broaden-and-build theory and affective neuroscience on the treatment of emotion dysfunctions and deficits in psychopathology', *Clinical Psychological Review*, November, 849–64

14 Thibodeau, P.H. (2016) 'A moist crevice for word aversion: in semantics not sounds', *PLOS ONE*, April, 157 [doi.org/10.1371/journal.pone.0153686]

15 Stephens, G.J. et al. (2010) 'Speaker–listener neural coupling underlies successful communication', *Proceedings of the National Academy of Sciences*, August, 14425–30

16 Zak, P. (2013) 'How stories change the brain', *Mind and Body*, December [greatergood.berkley.edu]

17 Campbell, J. (2012) *The Hero with a Thousand Faces*. Novato, CA: New World Library

'All things are subject
to interpretation.'

Friedrich Nietzsche

Philosopher, critic, poet and philologist
(1844–1900)

6: OUR BRAIN AND VISUAL PERCEPTION

 About this chapter

Our eyes take in most of the information that comes into our brain. But we cannot deal with every single visual input that we receive and so our visual perception is a continuous process of filtering, selecting and interpreting what we see.

In order to make sense of what we take in through our eyes, our brain uses its store of knowledge, beliefs, experiences and expectations as a reference guide. This means that we tend to screen in visual information that supports our view of the world, and screen out information that contradicts it. In effect, we see what we want and expect to see.

This chapter explains how our brain perceives visual information and constructs what we know as our reality.

Part 1: The science explained

How do we see?

Figure 6.1: How our brain *sees*

Our vision accounts for two-thirds of the electrical activity of the brain, and half of our neural tissue is directly or indirectly related to vision.[1] Vision is so dominant in the brain that it can affect, distort or even overwhelm our other senses.

Our ability to take in visual information depends on two of our organs: 1) *eyes* to receive visual stimuli and 2) *brain* to make

Visual input

sense of these stimuli. Our eyes generate a two-dimensional image but our brain needs a three-dimensional understanding in order for us to interact with the world around us.

The area most involved in visual processing is the occipital lobe at the back of the brain, as explained in Chapter 1, Our Brain.

When we receive a visual image from our optic nerve, the brain then adds two extra elements to this image: our existing memory and our interpretation of the image that we are currently seeing.

We are constantly comparing what we see with what we already know, and we often see only what we expect to see. This can make us blind to other items or objects in our visual field, as Chapter 4, Our Brain and Attention, discusses in more detail.

According to the psychologist Professor Richard Gregory, our visual perception is shaped both by our experiences and by our expectations, which enable us to make inferences about what is in front of us.[2] Because most of the visual information that we receive is lost by the time our brain processes it, our memories enable us to create best guesses or hypotheses. This process is known as *top-down processing* and it makes our reality almost entirely subjective.

We see the whole first and details second

When we see an object, it takes one-tenth of a second for the brain to process that information and make sense of it.[3]

For example, if we look at the picture on the left, we see a circle rather than a collection of dots.

Much of our understanding of how and why we perceive objects comes from *Gestalt psychology* (*gestalt* is from the German word for 'form' or 'shape'). The principle of Gestalt psychology is that we form wholes from parts of objects that can be separated and analysed. So the whole is different from the sum of its parts.

If we look at the *figure–ground* picture on the left, it can be perceived as two different images depending on how we see it: there are two faces looking at each other or a white vase. The figure is the object we perceive, while the ground is everything that is in the background. Our eyes separate the figure(s) from the background in order to understand what is being seen.

Many famous logos take advantage of the Gestalt psychology principle:

» In the **FedEx** logo, look for the arrow between the 'E' and the 'X'.

» In the **Formula 1** logo, look for the hidden number 1 between the letter 'F' and the speed lines.

» In the **Carrefour** logo, look for the white 'C' in the middle.

» In the **Hershey's Kisses** logo, look for the chocolate 'kiss' between the 'K' and the 'I'.

» In the **Toblerone** logo, look in the picture of the Matterhorn for the image of the bear, the symbol of the Swiss city of Berne.

» In the **Tour de France** logo, look for the cycling man; the yellow circle is a wheel.

When we look at an object, each of our eyes sees a slightly different picture. Our brain then brings together both versions. We use cues, such as shadows, textures and prior knowledge, to help us to judge depth and distance.

Our brain can process entire images in as few as 13 milliseconds, and it stores this information for later recall.[4]

We see faces everywhere

One of the reasons that we have survived as a species is because we can perceive and recognise *faces*.

As Chapter 2, Our Brain and Emotion, explains, we have an area of the brain dedicated to seeing faces. This area is called the *fusiform face area* (FFA) and it means, among other things, that we can quickly recognise someone we know, even from different perspectives.

We see faces everywhere – in clouds, shapes of leaves, drinks and food.[5] This phenomenon, called *pareidolia*, is believed to be a result of the brain's top-down processing tendency to use what is known and familiar.

Faces are encountered in every aspect of our life.

We see faces in trees.

 We see faces in buildings.

 We see faces in food.

 We see faces in games.

 We see faces in cars.

(Courtesy of Kent Area Midget & Sprite Club representative)

When we think we see a face in other objects, the activity in our brain – in both the *occipital lobe*, which processes visual information, and the *frontal lobe*, which is involved in planning and decision-making – is exactly the same as if we were in

In 2004, Diane Duyser in Florida, USA, made a toasted cheese sandwich and said that, when she looked at it before eating it, she saw a lady looking back at her.

Ten years later, the cheese sandwich was sold on eBay for $28,000 to an online casino that claimed that it would take the sandwich on a world tour and donate the money to charity.

fact looking at a real person. This may explain why we really believe we have seen a face.

Our tendency to see faces everywhere may be a survival instinct: our existence has depended on our ability to interact and cooperate with other human beings (and avoid dangerous animals). We are therefore hard-wired to seek out other people in our environment.

In fact, the wider our social network, the more the fusiform face area grows in the brain. So our brain continues to adapt to be able to recognise the people around us.

Blindness in our brain

People with damage to certain areas of the brain can develop a form of brain blindness, known as *agnosia*. Those who suffer from agnosia will be able to describe the features of an object such as a table, but will not be able to recognise it as a table.

For example, someone with agnosia may describe a rose as 'about six inches in length, a convoluted red form with a linear green attachment', but they do not know it as a *rose*.

One form of agnosia is a failure to recognise faces. This face blindness is known as *prosopagnosia*. People with prosopagnosia need to rely on other features such as voice, hairstyle or clothes to recognise people.

Prosopagnosia was explained in depth by neurologist Oliver Sachs, who described a patient suffering from prosopagnosia; the patient confused his wife's head with a hat and tried to put it (his wife's head) on his own head.[6]

We take shortcuts to simplify what we see

In order to help us concentrate on what is important, our brain takes shortcuts and simplifies the information our eyes receive. These shortcuts compensate for the delay in our brain's visual processing time. The simpler the object, the easier and faster it is for the brain to interpret what it is.

Even when we observe something complex, we still reorganise it into something simpler.

Consider the diagram below:

Compare the three separate objects (triangle, square, circle) on the right to the complex-looking white object on the left.

You may find that the three coloured objects are easier to distinguish than the white object, which appears to have no recognisable form.

Part 2: Impact on our daily life

We fill in the gaps

The brain likes to see a whole image first, before dealing with the composite details, as already discussed in this chapter.

Although we use our store of knowledge and memories to interpret new visual inputs, sometimes there is not an exact match between what we see and our stored information. In other words there is a gap. To help us to bridge this gap and complete the picture, we find a near match and use our brain to make associations. The less information, the more we provide our own material to address any disparities.

This is why we can construct a meaningful image from random shapes, as illustrated by our ability to form a panda's face from just some black shapes:

Our search for whole patterns is highlighted by the fact that we can make sense of the passage below:

Aoccdrnig to rscheearch at Cmabrigde Uinervtisy, it deosn't mttaer in waht oredr the ltteers in a wrod are, the olny iprmoetnt tihng is taht the frist and lsat ltteer be at the rghit pclae. The rset can be a toatl mses and you can sitll raed it wouthit porbelm. Tihs is bcuseae the huamn mnid deos not raed ervey lteter by istlef, but the wrod as a wlohe.

Visual perception is therefore dependent on context. Whether we see random shapes or a collection of letters or words, our brain will jump to a conclusion about what comes next; it then fills in the gaps to help us make sense of it.

Why are we susceptible to visual illusions?

The word *illusion* comes from the Latin word *illudere*, which means 'to mock'. When we see a visual illusion we often feel that our eyes are playing tricks on us.

Because of the speed at which our brain works, as well as the shortcuts it has to take to interpret visual information quickly, our brains are susceptible to being deceived.

An example of this is the *Müller-Lyer illusion* (Figure 6.2), which distorts our perception of the lower line to make it look longer than the line above it.

Figure 6.2: Müller-Lyer illusion

In the *Herring illusion* (Figure 6.3), the black left-to-right lines look warped, even though they are actually straight.

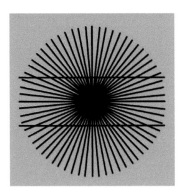

Figure 6.3: Herring illusion

Edward Adelson, Professor of Vision Science at the Massachusetts Institute of Technology (MIT), designed the chequerboard illusion (Figure 6.4) in 1995 to highlight how we determine colour with shadow.

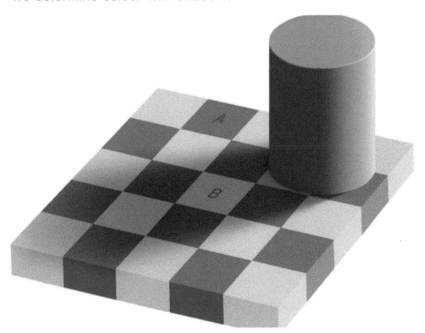

Figure 6.4: Chequerboard illusion
Credit: Professor Edward Adelson, MIT

Our brain knows that shadows make objects darker and then tries to compensate for this by interpreting shadowy objects as lighter than they actually are.

In the case of the chequerboard, we therefore assume that the square marked B is slightly darker than it should be because of the impact of the shadow. In fact A is the same colour as B.

If you still do not believe it, cut square B out of this book and put it on top of square A. You will see that they are in fact the same colour!

Our visual perception protects us . . .

We are very good at picking out similarities and differences in our world.

Our basic human instinct to protect ourselves from danger has stimulated our craving for similarity and sharpened our ability to detect anything different or unknown in our visual field.

Studies have even demonstrated that the more diverse our environment, the more we are drawn to and seek out people who are like us.[7] This may explain why many married couples look quite similar!

Being able to spot similarity across a range of people is known as the *similarity-attraction effect* (SAE). A recent study has shown that people are even likely to pick partners who share a similar DNA.[8]

Our experience of similarity also affects our assumptions about trustworthiness. Research shows that we are more likely to trust and treat favourably people who look like us, perhaps because we feel a greater genetic affiliation to them.

The reverse is also true: we are more likely to perceive facial similarity in those whom we consider trustworthy.[9]

. . . but can also prevent new thinking

The downside of our preference for similarity is that we may surround ourselves with a comfort zone of homogeneity and limit ourselves to interacting only with people who feel familiar to us.

The implications of this are significant, particularly in the light of research that reveals the strong relationship between diverse social networks and innovation – the more diverse the social network, the more innovation will occur.[10]

And so our natural inclination to feel safe and familiar may lead to constrained personal networks and reduced learning opportunities, compared to people from diverse backgrounds.

Our truth is subjective

Our lens of perception turns neutral information into events that are meaningful for us. This collectively constitutes our *truth*. This truth then becomes an internal guide of what is right, even though it may not be representative of what is actually there.

Our truth colours and distorts our perceptions to the extent that each of us might look at the same thing, but we will all see something different.

A group of young boys, some from wealthy families and some from poor families, were all asked to look carefully at a coin.[11] The coin was then taken away and all the boys were asked to draw a picture of it.

The boys from the wealthy families drew a smaller-sized coin than the boys from the poor families.

The boys' perception of the coin was therefore affected to some extent by the degree of importance given to money within each family.

The truth that we constantly project on to the world around us helps direct our attention to what is important and relevant.

This was explained in more depth in Chapter 4, Our Brain and Attention.

We do not see ourselves accurately

Our view of ourselves develops over time and is influenced by our culture, experiences and interactions with others.

In Western societies, it is now a social norm for women and men to be dissatisfied with their body shape and believe that their bodies are never thin or fit enough.[12] In fact, this social norm has extended to other countries such as Fiji, where the ideal physical female shape has shifted dramatically from voluptuous to thin – resulting in an extraordinary increase in eating disorders.[13]

Across the world, the reported increase in eating disorders and psychological problems such as body dysmorphic disorder (where we become unable to see ourselves accurately) are often blamed on the widespread influence of traditional and social media. The tragedy is that, according to a report by the Professional Association for Childcare and Early Years (PACEY) in 2016, children as young as three years old now have body confidence issues.

As Dr Jacqueline Harding, child development expert, comments:

'More research is needed in this area but contributing factors are likely to include: images on TV; images in storybooks and animations; the general chat by adults about their bodies, dieting, cosmetic surgery etc. There is little doubt that low levels of self-esteem appear to contribute significantly to negative perceptions of body image.'

Mirror, mirror on the wall

Our distorted view of our body also extends to our face. But it seems that here we are more likely to perceive ourselves in a more favourable light. When looking at pictures of our face, we identify ourselves more quickly with an image that has been airbrushed to look more attractive than an unaltered image.[14]

This distortion does not extend to our perception of others, whom we easily recognise from non-airbrushed images. So it seems that we are inclined towards a more attractive version of ourselves.

But what happens when mirrors on the wall reflect our image back?

Research has shown that people taking a test in a room with a mirror are less likely to cheat compared with control groups performing the same exercises in rooms without mirrors.

Mirrored settings, it seems, increase our ethical behaviour and the effort we put into our work.

Part 3: Stories and top tips

Our reality is what we are used to

In the 1800s, a Scottish missionary, Robert Laws, showed a picture to East Africans living in the country that is now Malawi.

While Westerners saw a family sitting in a cornered room with a window looking out on to a tree outside, East Africans saw a family sitting outside under a tree in the background and a woman carrying a box on her head.

Our perception of the world is shaped by our reality.

Whose truth is it anyway?

Over the last 50 years, the world's media has had a pervasive influence over what we believe. The advent of the Internet has sparked an explosion of real-time information on a global level. More information means more control and so the media operates like a giant brain, shaping our perceptions and opinions as well as determining the flow and content of messages.

For example, on 1 September 2016, the *Wall Street Journal* published two opposing headlines, both with the same picture:

» Trump Softens His Tone
» Trump Talks Tough on Wall

Claims were then made on the Internet that the *Wall Street Journal* had deliberately attempted to sway Republican readers with the first headline, 'Trump Softens His Tone', in a pro-Trump area and to use the other headline, 'Trump Talks Tough on Wall', in a non-Trump area in order to bolster Democratic support.

In fact, the two editions of the *Wall Street Journal* were published at different times of the day. The first was published after Trump's meeting with Mexican president Enrique Peña Nieto. The second was published later in the day, after Trump had delivered a speech about immigration and the building of a wall along Mexico's border with the United States.

So not only is our frame of reference constructed by the media, but the Internet is now also contributing an additional dynamic to the way we interpret the news we are given. Newspaper headlines shape our views initially and then citizen journalism provides another dimension.

Whatever their guise and format, the various media channels effectively control our reality. Our view of the world is continually being influenced, directed, manipulated and distorted by what we read and hear.

For instance, our views of various recent events across the world, such as the 2016 presidential election in the United States, Brexit and the Syrian crisis, are fashioned by the techniques used by all forms of media and Internet communications. Our emotions are regularly aroused and manipulated and we create heroes and villains on the strength of selective reporting and public mass-messaging.

Because we are so easily swayed by the views of others, sometimes without even realising it, we find ourselves being swept along and adopting their opinions as our own.

Fact, fiction or just fake?

Fake news describes online articles and stories that look like authentic journalism but are completely fabricated to resemble journalism and attract as much attention as possible. The recent circulation of fake news typifies the danger of believing what we read.

One of the best-known examples of fake news is the story that aired in December 2016, about a man brandishing a gun in a Washington pizzeria that had been reported as being the headquarters of a child sex ring run by Hillary Clinton. The story was reported on online message boards and a poll reported that 14% of Trump supporters believed its validity.

A BuzzFeed analysis has claimed that fake election news stories generated more interest and engagement on Facebook, where there is an audience of around 1.8 billion, than stories from traditional major news outlets such as the *New York Times*, *Washington Post*, *Huffington Post* and NBC News. Facebook has now announced that it will be providing tips to help readers spot fake news stories.

The dangers of our digital age

 Our digital age may have created significant efficiencies in commerce and communication, but it has also brought with it a new kind of interaction that is no longer based on physical human presence.

Although our brain is still designed to look for and interpret facial expression, body language and tonal variation, the preferred mode of interaction now through social media means that people see and are seen virtually, and not face-to-face.

For our young and future generations, it seems that perceptions are now managed almost entirely though social media. Connections are made in order to expand networks but are then narrowed down to shared interests. Friends are categorised, images are carefully crafted and managed, and the need to belong, be accepted and be admired is addictive.

But the proliferation of social media sites showing off personal images is exacerbating a need to look perfect and manage how other people perceive us. Images are airbrushed before being posted, and teenagers are now caught in a complex paradox of wanting to fit in and to stand out, to wear make-up but also look natural, to follow others and be followed themselves. And sadly, even though they are more connected than ever, they often feel isolated and alone.

It is therefore crucial that we regularly give ourselves a healthy dose of reality. There will always be people who seem richer, thinner, cleverer, fitter and more successful than we are.

Being happy starts with accepting this and appreciating what we do have.

In the words of Lao Tzu:

> **'Be content with what you have; rejoice in the way things are. When you realise there is nothing lacking, the whole world belongs to you.'**

Imagine new possibilities and approaches by looking around you and keeping your mind open and receptive. Learn something new on a regular basis. Put your ego away: it may be encouraging a blinkered view of life.

Manage the way you receive information. Have checks and balances in place when looking at information. Our brains are prone to errors in perception. Find people who do not necessarily agree with you. Their lens may prevent you from making a mistake.

Accept who you are, with all your imperfections. We are all a work in progress! Some degree of self-criticism and humility are fundamental to learning and personal growth. At the same time, recognise the pressure that social media puts us all under when it comes to comparison with others. Even *perfect* people are not perfect! But we can all strive for fulfilment and satisfaction in everything we do.

Gain new perspectives by challenging your own truth and the way you look at a situation. Be careful of justifying your position and beliefs, even in the face of contradictory evidence. It is easier to form a new belief than change an existing one. Challenge the way you perceive difficult situations: another approach may help you address these better.

Exercise and stretch your cognitive abilities by challenging your view of the world. Visual illusions, as well as being entertaining and fun, are effective ways to stretch our thinking. They also remind us that our mind is easily tricked and that our perception is not always matched by reality.

References for Chapter 6

1 Bowan, M.D. (1999) 'Integrating vision with the other senses', monograph chapter in OEP Foundation post-graduate curriculum, December, 1–10

2 Gregory, R. (1970) *The Intelligent Eye*. London: Weidenfeld and Nicolson

3 Maus, G.W. (2013) 'Motion-dependent representation of space in area', *Neuron*, May, 554–62

4 Potter, M.C. et al. (2014) 'Detecting meaning in RSVP at 13 ms per pictures', *Attention, Perception and Psychophysics*, February, 270–79

5 Liu, J. (2014) 'Seeing Jesus in toast: neural and behavioral correlates of face pareidolia', *Cortex*, April, 60–77

6 Sachs, O. (2015) *The Man Who Mistook His Wife for a Hat*. London: Picador

7 Bahns, A. et al. (2011) 'Social ecology of similarity. Big schools, small schools and social relationships', *Group Processes and Intergroup Relations*, July, 119–31

8 Domingue, B.W. (2014) 'Genetic and educational assortative mating among US adults', *Proceedings for the National Academy of Sciences*, April, 7996–8000

9 Farmer, H. (2013) 'Trust in me: trustworthy others are seen as more physically similar to the self', *Psychological Science*, October, 290–92

10 Philips, K. (2014) 'How diversity makes us smarter: being around people who are different from us makes us more creative, more diligent and harder-working', *Scientific American*, October, 311

11 Bruner, J.S. & C.C. Goodman (1947) 'Value and need as organizing factors in perception', *Journal of Abnormal and Social Psychology*, January, 33–44

12 Salk, R. & E.E. Engeln-Maddox (2011) '"If you're fat, then I'm humongous!" Frequency, content, and impact of fat talk among college women', *Psychology of Women Quarterly*, April, 18–28

13 Gerbasi, M.E. et al. (2014) 'Globalization and eating disorder risk: peer influence, perceived social norms, and adolescent disordered eating in Fiji', *International Journal of Eating Disorders*, November, 727–37

14 Epley, N. and W. Whitchurch (2008) 'Mirror, mirror on the wall: enhancement in self-recognition', *The Personality and Social Psychology Bulletin*, November, 1159–70

'There is no neutrality. There is only greater or lesser awareness of one's bias.'

Phyllis Rose

Literary critic, essayist, biographer and educator

(1942–)

7: OUR BRAIN AND BIASES

 About this chapter

Being biased is a human phenomenon. We are all biased and we use our biases every day, often unconsciously, to help us make decisions.

Biases are the beliefs, attitudes and preferences that we form about ourselves and other people. We pick up these biases through our culture, background and education and they are pervasive influences over how we see the world and make decisions.

Our brain has to predict rapidly what is safe or harmful in our environment. To help our brain do this, our biases quickly shortcut new information. The problem is that they intervene so quickly that we may make a bad choice or overlook a crucial detail.

This chapter explains how biases work in our brain and shows how our biases may distort our thinking or prevent us from forming an accurate view of the world.

Part 1: The science explained

A psychological immune system in the brain

Our biases are human adaptive responses to our environment and provide an immediate frame of reference for fast interpretation and action.

In a sense, our biases are our brain's psychological immune system and prevent us from decision paralysis.[1] If we were unable to respond quickly to our surroundings we would not be able to survive.

Figure 7.1: We are all biased

Why are our biases so powerful?

Even in situations when we have limited information, we still have to make decisions based on what we think we know. We may later rationalise our initial assumption and use information we gather after the event in order to endorse or justify our first belief or decision. If subsequent information then contradicts our first response, we generally find a way to make this new evidence fit with our original belief, however incongruent it is. And if we cannot make it fit, we will dismiss it altogether. Psychologists call this tendency *motivated reasoning*.

Because our views often become so polarised, we place little value on facts that threaten our existing beliefs. In politically motivated reasoning we may even resort to conspiratorial thinking that helps us cement our views about the other side. It is easier for us to assume a *cover-up* of information than to change a deeply entrenched belief.

Linked to motivated reasoning is another psychological phenomenon known as *cognitive dissonance*. Cognitive dissonance occurs when we hold two beliefs that are conflicting and this creates a tension in our brain that we have to resolve.

Often we find a way of justifying our action. This is why we make excuses for eating food that we know is unhealthy ('I will go the gym tomorrow') or smoking ('more people die in road accidents than from smoking-related illnesses'). We find a way to restore the balance and reinterpret evidence to fit with what feels comfortable to us.

Both motivated reasoning and cognitive dissonance feed and strengthen our biases.

Types of biases

Loss aversion

 One of our strongest biases is called *loss aversion*. Professor Daniel Kahneman explains that this bias is based on the fact that our brain has to minimise uncertainty about the future and places more urgency on avoiding threats than realising gains.[2] This has led to the powerful influence of potential losses on our behaviour.

Whenever we can, we try to avoid losses, and we hate losing more than we like winning. Consequently, we do not weigh gains against losses equally. It is also mentally harder for people to convert from losses to gains: once people have developed a negative view of something it takes a long time for them to consider the same thing in a positive way.

As a result of loss aversion, people are more inclined to spend money on something if they know that they will lose if they do not spend the money. Some studies suggest that psychological losses are generally twice as powerful as gains. When we buy something, we like to feel that our pain of loss (paying) must be offset by what we will gain.

Loss aversion is responsible for the *sunk-cost fallacy*, which means that the more we invest in something, the harder it becomes to abandon it. This is why we often convince ourselves that further investment is justified because the resources already invested will otherwise be lost. And that is not taking into consideration the overall losses involved in the further investment.

The sunk-cost fallacy explains why projects are kept going for longer than they should: we cannot face the thought of having to stop them after so much investment has already been made.

> The sunk-cost fallacy is sometimes called the *Concorde fallacy*. Concorde was the world's first commercial supersonic aeroplane and was a joint venture between Air France and British Airways. Despite early predictions that it would be a financial failure, the project was continued. People's psychological attachment to their initial investment meant that no one wanted to give up, even after huge losses of time, effort and money.

Confirmation bias

Confirmation bias is a form of selection bias, whereby we look for and choose information that confirms or reinforces our existing beliefs. We tend to assign more weight to supporting evidence and ignore or downplay any contradictory evidence we receive. Confirmation bias originates from the influence of our desire to prove our beliefs: when we want or expect something to be true, we often make it true.

With confirmation bias enabled, we see only what we expect or want to see. As a result, we respond more to the behaviour of those who confirm our own views. In this way, if we assume that people will behave negatively towards us, we will tend to interpret their behaviour, even if it is neutral, as hostile.

Confirmation bias can be dangerous since it can blind us to other avenues or possibilities. The past is not always the best predictor of the future and it may prevent us from seeking different information, or even lead us to the wrong conclusion.

Specialists and experts are particularly susceptible to confirmation bias. For example, a doctor may jump straight to a particular hypothesis about a certain illness and then ask the patient questions that help to confirm that hypothesis. The doctor may also ignore any evidence the patient might provide that may contradict the hypothesis. Similarly, lawyers taking on a new case may see shared traits with a previous case and look for details to support the assumption that both are the same – even when they are not.

> During Hurricane Katrina in 2005, thousands of residents of New Orleans ignored signs that the levee system was collapsing. They did not believe that this could happen and so were unable to interpret any information that contradicted their beliefs. Consequently, they stayed in their homes, which were directly in the line of the oncoming water. Katrina claimed nearly 2,000 lives.

Optimism bias

Optimism bias leads us to overestimating our likelihood of experiencing good events in our lives and underestimating our likelihood of experiencing bad events. Optimism bias also means that we are over-optimistic about ourselves in particular – and rarely about other people. And often we are oblivious to this fact.

The benefit of optimism bias is that it can protect and inspire us – and it keeps us moving forward. For instance, when we are successful, we believe it is because of our ability and when we fail, we blame circumstances beyond our control – which prevents us from giving up.

When we are optimistic, we look into the future with hope. This is why many of us prefer a working day such as Friday, which brings with it the anticipation of the weekend, over a day of holiday such as Sunday, which heralds the beginning of the working week. In other words, optimism bias feeds our anticipation for what is coming rather than our pleasure in what is right in front of us. Being optimistic also helps us to reduce anxiety and stress.

However, unrealistic optimism can lead to risky behaviour such as smoking, despite scientific evidence and statistics that clearly point to its harmful effects. Unrealistic optimism can even lead to poor financial planning and inaccurate estimates about the cost and duration of projects.

A study asked a sample of smokers and non-smokers to estimate the likelihood that they would live to age 75 or longer.[3] Researchers compared the estimates with a representative sample of death certificates.

The estimates were accurate except for those submitted by heavy smokers: men reported a 50% likelihood of living to age 75 and women reported a 60% likelihood of living to age 75.

When compared with the death certificates, the results showed that only 26% of men and 30% of such women would actually survive to age 75.

Overconfidence bias

Closely linked to optimism bias is *overconfidence bias*. Overconfidence bias is observed when we make judgements about ourselves relative to other people. When we are overconfident about our abilities to make good judgements, we often do a poor job of estimating probability and make bad decisions as a result. This bias is sometimes referred to as the *illusion of knowledge* bias because we are more confident in our knowledge and ability than we deserve to be.

Overconfidence bias may explain why only 10% of New Year's resolutions made in January will be maintained until the following December.

And if we think that we are not affected in any way by the overconfidence bias, it means we are overconfident!

In 2015, a leadership consultancy conducted a large research project involving 69,000 leaders and 750,000 employees.[4] Leaders were asked to rate their skills and abilities, then their ratings were compared to how their people viewed them.

The results showed that there was little positive correlation between leaders' and employees' ratings. In fact, those leaders who believed that they were exceptional were in fact judged by employees to be among the worst leadership performers.

Conversely, leaders who underestimated how good they were turned out to be best at their jobs in the eyes of their employees.

The more they underrated themselves, the higher other people rated them.

Self-awareness and emotional intelligence are frequently touted in boardrooms as essential leadership skills – but perhaps leaders also need a healthy dose of self-criticism too.

Present bias

We do not do a good job of planning for the future. This has been illustrated in studies that ask people their decisions about the future versus the present.

Present bias describes our tendency to place more emphasis on benefits that are lodged in the present time when considering a trade-off with a future point in time.

Present bias is related to a cognitive trap known as *hyperbolic discounting*, where we are less likely to consider the consequences of our choices the further in the future these choices are. This is why we often struggle to save money today, or why our food choices today may look significantly different to the savings and food choices that we plan for the future. For example, we are more likely to choose food that gives us pleasure today – such as chocolate – over food that offers less pleasure but is considered a healthier option.

Because we have such a strong present bias and often feel disconnected from the future, researchers have looked at what it would take to get us to save more money now.[5]

People were shown either images of their current self or aged images depicting how they may look in the future. They were then asked to allocate $1,000 among four options:

1 Buying something nice for someone special
2 Investing in a retirement fund
3 Planning a fun event
4 Putting money into a savings account

Those who saw an image of their aged self put twice as much money into the retirement fund as those who saw the image of their current self.

In-group and out-group bias

 Our brain is designed to seek out similarities and differences in others, as Chapter 6, Our Brain and Visual Perception, explains. We naturally and subconsciously favour people in our own social group because similarity feels familiar and safe.

Our *in-groups* are people with whom we feel we share several traits or interests, such as our family and people from the same culture. *Out-groups* are people who are different from us.

Social prejudice and racism are rooted in in-group bias. Some scientists believe that this bias is hard-wired in our brains.

The neuroscientist Dr David Eagleman conducted an fMRI study where he asked 130 participants to look at six labelled hands which were then randomly stabbed by a syringe.[6] This stabbing activated a brain response. Researchers wanted to see whether people would care differently if they observed someone from their in-group being stabbed versus someone from their out-group.

There was a strong brain response when observing any in-group member being stabbed by the syringe, and no response when the out-group member was stabbed.

The study shows that we find it more difficult to empathise with those whom we believe are different to us.

Negativity bias

Our brain reacts more intensely to negative than positive stimuli. This feeds our natural *negativity bias*. We are more likely to reach for bad news than good news and we also attribute more weight and significance to negative rather than positive comments.

From an evolutionary point of view, our negativity bias is a protective measure that has ensured our survival. We have adapted to be able to spot threat and danger in our world so that we can stay alive. Despite this, we need to be vigilant as this bias can sometimes cloud our thinking by making us assume the worst.

When we apply our negativity bias to our own life, it can promote negative self-esteem which can even affect our physical health. This was shown in a study about normal-sized teenagers who believed themselves to be overweight – they were found to be more likely to become obese in later life.[7]

Can a positive or negative attitude affect team performance?

This question was considered in a study that looked at the performance of 60 business teams.[8] The study examined the relationship between the number of positive/negative comments made between team members and the team performance overall.

The findings showed a marked correlation between team performance and positive comments. In fact, the positive comments in the high-performing teams outweighed negative comments by nearly six to one. The medium-performing teams showed a ratio of nearly two positive comments to one negative comment. The low-performing teams showed that three negative comments were made for every positive one.

Our negativity bias is therefore far-reaching and can infiltrate all aspects of our life: our self-esteem, relationships and the language we use.

Groupthink

We strive for consensus within a group. *Groupthink* is a bias that we adopt when we set aside our own personal beliefs in order to adopt the opinion of the rest of the group. This can lead to people being overly optimistic, engaging in risk-taking and ignoring possible moral problems, warning signs or consequences.

Groupthink can lead to faulty decisions by the collective. A team or group will be particularly vulnerable to groupthink when that group is highly cohesive, isolated from external influences, lacking leadership and when its members are from similar backgrounds.

In the 1950s Solomon Asch conducted a series of
psychological experiments to examine the power of
group opinion over an individual's opinion.[9] People were
shown a line drawing (Exhibit 1) and asked to select a
matching line from a group of lines of different lengths
(Exhibit 2).

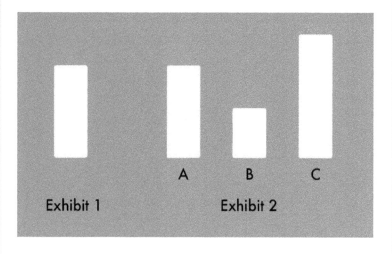

Exhibit 1   A   B   C

Exhibit 2

Participants were asked in a group to select the
matching line. Actors were present within the group
and were briefed to choose a different line at certain
intervals – even though their choice was an obviously
incorrect answer. On the occasions that the actors
selected the wrong answer, the participants were
unwilling to challenge the group and were more
prepared to give an incorrect answer in order to fit
in, even though they knew the answer was wrong.

When they were asked why they had conformed to the
wishes of the group, some admitted knowing that the
answer was wrong but said they did not want to be

ridiculed; others said that they thought that the rest of the group must be correct.

Asch's experiment shows the degree to which groupthink and a desire to conform is driven by both a need to fit in and a belief that other people collectively must be better informed.

Anticipation of regret

An *a priori*, or *anticipation of possible regret*, can influence our decision-making. This is often seen in buying decisions where we may later regret not choosing one of the options that was available. Anticipation of regret can therefore influence choices made at the time and can lead to faulty decision-making, even outweighing risk perception.

We can see this tendency in bidding behaviour at auctions. We behave differently when we cannot see the price that others are offering, compared to when we see what others are offering, particularly in incremental stages. In the latter case (when we can see what others are bidding), we are more likely to offer a higher figure than we had previously intended, in order to avoid the feeling that we have just missed out on something. We are therefore trying to mitigate the regret we may otherwise have felt, had we lost the bidding war.

Anticipation of regret was observed in 1998 when Andrew Wakefield and colleagues published an article in *The Lancet*, highlighting a link between autism and bowel disorders with the measles, mumps and rubella (MMR) inoculation.[10]

Parents anticipated the regret that they felt they would have if they had their child inoculated. It was better, in their eyes, to do nothing (and risk measles, mumps and rubella for their child) than feel that they were the potential cause of autism or a bowel disorder by having the child vaccinated, even though there was scientific evidence proving that the triple vaccination was safe.

The Lancet article was later retracted.

Learned helplessness

Learned helplessness is a psychological trap and a form of conditioning whereby people feel that they have no control over their situation and so behave in a helpless manner. This inactive state can prevent them from seeing opportunities for relief or change.

The concept of learned helplessness was discovered by accident in dogs by two psychologists, Martin Seligman and Steven Maier.[11] The dogs had been conditioned to expect an electrical shock after hearing a certain tone.

➤

After the conditioning, the dogs were placed in a box that contained two compartments separated by a low barrier. The floor in one of the compartments was electrified and the dogs only had to jump over the barrier to escape being given an electric shock. But the dogs did not jump. Further experiments showed that these dogs had developed a cognitive expectation that nothing they did would prevent or eliminate the shocks. They therefore made no attempt to escape the shocks.

Since this experiment, this phenomenon has been observed in various situations involving humans, where an earlier failure leads to feelings of powerlessness and impotence that affect future performance.

Learned helplessness can induce the pessimism-attribution bias that leads to distorted thinking and self-beliefs. For example, when we have failed at something we may then become convinced that nothing we do from then on will have any effect on future performance.

This is often the reason why people stay in the wrong job or the wrong relationship, or why they do nothing to improve their health. To an outsider, a solution may seem simple but for people suffering from this bias it is often difficult to escape the bad situation because they feel that it is beyond their control.

Part 2: Impact on our daily life

We think other people are more biased than we are

Many of us would like to believe that our opinions and decisions have been carefully and rationally formed. But all of us are biased to some degree or other – and all of us will experience some or all of the biases explained above. Yet, ironically, many of us think other people are more biased than we are!

Figure 7.2: Our biases influence how we see the world

Much of the time we are unaware of our own biases. This is known as *unconscious* or *implicit bias*. Even if we do recognise that we may be biased, we rarely question or confront the biases we carry inside us. Nevertheless, our biases continue to influence how we live and interact with those around us.

Despite being aware of our biases, we can never fully overcome our biased thinking; but we can try to interrupt it, slow it down and minimise its effects on our decision-making.

The key point to remember is that no amount of training will fully eradicate biased thinking. The best we can do is to become more self-aware and recognise that we have biases, so that we can challenge our own thinking and assumptions.

We hate being wrong

Although we like to think that we make good decisions and that if we were presented with contradictory facts we would change our views, in fact the opposite is true.

As discussed earlier in this chapter, when we are provided with evidence to counter an original opinion or belief, we stick even more rigidly to our original belief, rather than believe the new contradictory (but correct) evidence.

We are so afraid of being wrong that we lose our ability to reason when someone or something contradicts our convictions. Not even the proof of Barack Obama's birth certificate has been sufficient to change some people's beliefs that he was not born in the United States. By the same token, many of the parents who were convinced by the link between the MMR vaccine and autism did not change their views even after this link was found to be false; in fact many parents became even less likely to vaccinate their children.

Our brain avoids complexity

The more choices we have, the more we avoid complexity and the less likely we are to make a decision. Because most of us dislike uncertainty, and our brain is continually attempting to predict and protect, when there are too many unknowns we look for the simplest solution to help us make a fast decision.

When we have to choose between multiple outcomes, our brain cannot cope and becomes distracted. However, when we have just two outcomes, we are able to make a much faster choice.

More choice is not always better for our brain! In a study shoppers in a food store saw a display stand with 24 varieties of jam being offered.[12] Later in the week, shoppers saw a similar stand but with only six varieties of jam.

Although the larger stand initially attracted more interest than the smaller stand, people were ten times more likely to purchase a jar of jam from the smaller rather than the larger display.

Having too many choices also makes us tired and can even lead to us avoiding having to make a decision altogether. This is called *choice overload* [13] and can lead us to *choice paralysis*, where we avoid making important decisions.

As the number of options increases, the more the degree of certainty is reduced concerning the choice we have. As a result, we are more likely to suffer from anticipation of regret about the choice we may then go on to make.

We are easily influenced

Our brain is often influenced in ways of which we are often not aware. This has promoted interest in a topic known as *behavioural economics* or *decision science*. In fact, Harvard

University now offers an executive programme in Behavioural Economics in recognition of its importance.

Anchoring

Numbers matter! Our brain *anchors* itself to the highest available number. The initial figure we set for anything tends to influence the final price that is agreed. Our brain uses the initial number as the reference point. This is why we are more likely to pay more for something if we see a higher figure first. This explains why car prices in garages are so high: when the salesman then reduces the price, we feel like we have a deal. We can see the same effect when negotiating our salary for a new job and why we, not our new employer, should open negotiations. The higher we set the initial anchor, the higher the final agreed salary will be.

Framing

We can use language to *frame* choices that highlight either the positive or negative aspects of the same concept, which can then lead to different decisions. For example, would we prefer to undergo surgery with a 10% failure rate, or surgery with a 90% success rate?

Frames make the buying decision easy for the brain. Negative framing is used a great deal in marketing (playing to our loss aversion) – we are often told what we stand to lose if we choose not to purchase something. This has been discussed in Chapter 5, Our Brain and Language.

If we are buying a bottle of shampoo, we may have the chance to buy one bottle at a 20% discount or another bottle at full price with free conditioner. Because of our loss aversion, we are more likely to choose the bottle with the free gift, even though the value of the conditioner may be less than that of the discount. This is because we do not want to lose out on the free gift.

Priming

 Priming is a form of implicit or non-declarative memory (explained in more detail in Chapter 3, Our Brain and Memory) and it describes certain associations that we make based on the information we have already stored in our brain. For example, a person who hears the word *red* and is then asked to name a fruit may be more inclined to say 'strawberry' or 'apple' than a fruit that is not red.

We are constantly being primed in various ways.

» At the cinema, we are often primed to buy drinks, both as we walk into the cinema and during the commercials.

» In wine merchants, the music being played may influence us to buy wine from the same country as the music.

» In supermarkets, the smell of bread at the back of a store primes us to walk through the whole store.

» Smells associated with hygiene (such as citrus) may induce more hygienic behaviour.

» The colours green and blue can promote creative thinking. Offices that look out over green fields, rather than over concrete buildings, can have an impact on our ability to think up new ideas.

» Even putting a pen in our mouth horizontally can create a smile expression, which will make us feel happier and help us find jokes funnier!

Nudge theory

Nudge theory is an aspect of behavioural economics where our behaviour can be *nudged* in a specific direction. The direction can be either good or bad.

In 2010, the government in the United Kingdom set up the Behavioural Insights Team, who are also known as the Nudge Unit, and have worked with Richard Thaler whose best-selling book *Nudge* reinforces the same philosophy.[14]

In 2012, after winning the Civil Service Award, the Behavioural Insights Team published their **EAST** framework:

Easy   Make it as straightforward as possible for people to pay tax, debts or take up a service. Provide default options or pre-populated forms. Simplify the language used.

Attractive   Draw people's attention to important information or actions required of them up front. Design compelling rewards. Personalise language and make the message relevant to them.

Social   Describe what other people are doing, such as '9 out of 10 people pay their tax on time'. Actively incentivise or reward behaviour that saves time or money.

Timely   Prompt people when they are most receptive and likely to be honest. Give people the costs and benefits of their action and help them plan.

Among the initiatives of the Behavioural Insights Team has been one nudging people into paying their car's road tax using a letter written in simple English. It states: 'Pay your tax or lose your car.' In some cases, a photograph of the recipient's own car has been attached. This letter alone has doubled the number of people paying the tax, with the number tripling with the addition of the photograph.

Similar outcomes have been seen elsewhere.

Children may also be nudged. *The Economist* cites a study in French schools that found that if the subject was called 'geometry', boys excelled, but if it was called 'drawing', girls did just as well as the boys – or even better.[15]

Workplace studies have shown that managers who believe their company has a reputation for supporting women in more male-dominated fields of science and technology, are more likely to hire, develop and promote women.[16]

The downside of nudge is that we can also be manipulated in the same way by the nudging of others. By not paying attention to whether something is an *opt-in* or *opt-out*, we may find ourselves committing unknowingly to initiatives without even realising that we have done so.

For example, our tendency to accept default options means that we are more likely to enrol in schemes that have an opt-out rather than an opt-in clause. Taking organ donation as an example, a scheme that requires donors to state positively that they want their organs to be used (opt-in) has a lower sign-up rate than if donors are required to state if they do not want their organs to be used (opt-out). Similarly, in order to increase retirement savings, British legislation now supports the default option for corporate pension plans, which automatically enrols employees unless they choose to opt out.

Part 3: Stories and top tips

Even children become biased quickly

In the United States in 1968, the day after the assassination of Martin Luther King, one of the most significant social studies on in-group/out-group bias was carried out in an Iowa classroom.[17]

The teacher, Jane Elliot, decided to demonstrate racial prejudice by dividing her third-grade class into groups on the basis of eye colour. Elliot told the blue-eyed children that they were 'better' than the brown-eyed children and within minutes the blue-eyed children started calling their brown-eyed classmates 'stupid' and refused to play with them. The next day she reversed the situation and observed the brown-eyed children doing exactly the same to their blue-eyed classmates.

The impact of her classroom study had lasting effects: her pupils later showed significantly less racism than other children their own age, and this effect lasted as they grew to adulthood.

Jane Elliot has since run similar experiments on adults and has found that adults demonstrate even greater racist tendencies than children.

Who are our friends?

Many of us are living examples of in-group/out-group bias. We only have to look at the people we socialise with to observe this. Even when we think we have expanded horizons and have a heterogeneous social circle, we will nevertheless generally revert to what feels familiar and similar whenever our comfort zone is threatened.

In other words, we will naturally and automatically seek out people with whom we can identify and share some commonality, even in diverse surroundings.

Our friends therefore often reflect the type of people that we are ourselves.

Do we ever learn from our mistakes?

In 1672, a group of young girls in Salem Village in colonial Massachusetts started to blame their own bad behaviour on other people, whom they accused of being witches.

The Puritan community to which these girls belonged had formed a cohesive group, united by harsh winters, recent conflict, strong religious convictions and their belief in the occult.

Most of those accused were women who did not conform with the rest of the group and who were viewed as a threat to the community because they wore different clothes, challenged their husbands or, as widows, owned property. As a result of the legal trials in Salem, some 20 people and one dog were executed, with a further 200 people imprisoned.

None of these trials were based on any scientific evidence but rather were the result of widespread scapegoating and group polarisation by a community that was swept along on a wave of mass hysteria and accusation.

Centuries later, during the 1950s, Senator John McCarthy conducted a series of witch-hunts in search of communist sympathisers. Those who were accused were told to testify or risk losing their jobs and social standing. They were also offered the chance to cooperate and accuse some of their own friends and colleagues of being communists. Few people dared to challenge McCarthy's accusations.

During this time, people were suspicious and paranoid. The Cold War was the perfect breeding ground for groupthink and mass hysteria. Few people dared to speak out against McCarthy or his supporters, and no one at the time challenged the inaccurate reporting of the media or the death sentences, even though they were based on spurious evidence.

The McCarthy era, as it become known, prompted Arthur Miller to write *The Crucible* to highlight the parallels between McCarthyism and the events in Salem so many years earlier.

Although we like to think we learn from the past, we rarely ever do.

Being human makes us biased

During the 2016 US presidential election, Donald Trump's running mate Governor Mike Pence criticised Hillary Clinton for accusing police officers of having implicit biases, saying that it was demeaning and racist.

However, according to researchers such as Alexis McGill Johnson of the Perception Institute, Pence has confused implicit or unconscious bias with explicit or overt racism; having implicit bias is very much part of being human.

Although initiatives in recent years have focused on educating social institutions such as schools and businesses on implicit bias, it is a concept that nevertheless remains misunderstood in certain circles.

But accepting that we are all biased does not give us carte blanche to behave in a racist or bigoted manner, or relieve us of social responsibility. Even the best intentioned among us hold implicit biases. This does not mean that we are racist and are going to violate the rights of others; we all simply need to recognise that we naturally absorb these biases from the people and culture around us, and we often do so without questioning the biases' validity or morality.

Accept that biases exist in all of us – they make us human. You will then be more open to challenging your own biases. Question your judgements about others. A standard tool that is now commonly used to enable us to understand our own biases is the Implicit Association Test.

Nurture diversity in your world and travel as much as possible to learn about different cultures and customs. Our brain will adapt to different influences, such as diverse environments and multicultural perspectives.

Give your brain fewer options. This will help your decision-making. Think about how you are being nudged or influenced. Prime yourself with positive emotions, words and images.

Listen to the way you communicate with other people and pay constant attention to your own natural negativity bias. Behaviour influences thoughts, and thoughts influence behaviour. Be warm and positive in the way you act towards people and you will foster positive relationships, even with those you may previously have disregarded or written off.

Encourage healthy debate and disagreement. This will help defend against groupthink. Challenge your own expectations and beliefs about people. Beware of labelling individuals and of contributing towards stereotypical thinking. People normally behave in the way we expect them to behave.

References for Chapter 7

1 Gilbert, D. et al. (1998) 'Immune neglect: a source of durability bias in affective forecasting', *Journal of Personality and Social Psychology*, September, 617–38

2 Kahneman, D. (2012) *Thinking Fast and Slow*. London: Penguin Books

3 Schoenbaum, M. (1997) 'Do smokers understand the mortality effects of smoking? Evidence from the Health and Retirement Survey', *American Journal of Public Health*, May, 755–59

4 Zenger, J. & J. Folkman (2015) 'We like leaders who underrate themselves', *Harvard Business Review*, November, 2–6

5 Ersner-Hershfield, H. (2013) 'You make better decisions if you "see" your senior self', *Harvard Business Review*, June, 3–4

6 Eagleman, D. (2016) 'Why do I need you?', episode 5 of *The Brain*, aired February, BBC Four

7 Sutin, A. & A. Terracciano (2013) '"Weightism" increases risk for becoming, staying obese', *PLOS ONE*, 24 July [doi.org/10.1371/journal.pone.0070048]

8 Fredrickson, B. L. & M.F. Losada (2011) 'Positive affect and the complex dynamics of human flourishing', *American Psychologist*, October, 678–86

9 Asch, S. (1955) 'Opinions and social pressure', *Scientific American*, November, 31–35

10 Wakefield, A.J. (1998) 'RETRACTED: Ileal-lymphoid-nodular hyperplasia, non-specific colitis, and pervasive developmental disorder in children', *The Lancet*, February, 637–41

11 Seligman, M. & S. Maier (1967) 'Failure to escape traumatic shock', *Journal of Experimental Psychology*, May, 1–9

12 Lyengar, S. & M. Lepper (2000) 'When choice is demotivating: can one desire too much of a good thing?', *Personality Processes and Individual Differences*, December, 995–1006

13 Chernev, A. et al. (2015) 'Choice overload: A conceptual review and meta-analysis', *Journal of Consumer Psychology*, August, 333–58

14 Thaler, R. (2009) *Nudge: Improving Decisions about Health, Wealth and Happiness*. London: Penguin Books

15 *The Economist* (2012) 'Nudge, nudge, think, think', May [economist.com]

16 Braun, S. & R.A. Turner (2014) 'Attitudes and company practices as predictors of managers' intentions to hire, develop, and promote women in science, engineering, and technology professions', *Consulting Psychology Journal: Practice and Research*, June, 93–117

17 Peters, E.S. (1987) *A Class Divided: Then and Now*. London: Yale University Press

'Every child is an artist.
The problem is staying an
artist when you grow up.'

Pablo Picasso

Painter, sculptor, poet and playwright
(1881–1973)

8: OUR BRAIN AND CREATIVITY

 About this chapter

Our ability to think creatively has ensured our survival as a species. We have a natural curiosity that has led to new discoveries, and we have continued to forge new ways of living, communicating, eating, travelling and learning.

In recent years, as certain organisations have failed to keep up with or ahead of competitors, *creativity* and *innovation* have become popular concepts that are now generally viewed as the panacea for business success.

This emphasis on instilling or accessing a creative mind-set has prompted researchers, educators and business leaders to look more deeply at what *creativity* actually means and whether in fact everyone is capable of being creative.

This chapter discusses what creativity is and how it works in our brain. The underpinning premise is that we all have a creative spark that, in many of us, just needs to be reignited.

Part 1: The science explained

How does creativity work in our brain?

Figure 8.1: Creativity is a 'whole-brain' process

Creativity comprises the conception, testing and verifying of an idea. Creativity often happens when we are daydreaming, allowing our mind to wander, or even trying to imagine what other people are thinking. And an idea can come to us when we least expect it.

There are many mistaken beliefs about creativity. We convince ourselves that creativity is something other *creative* people are born with, that we have to be right-brained or left-handed, or that it is all about intellect. However, a commonly held view among researchers, innovators and artists is that, whoever we are and whatever our skill, we can all be creative; we just need courage, perseverance and the willingness to fail.

Chapter 1, Our Brain, describes our brain as bilaterally organised to process different types of information, with creativity featured on the right side. Although the right side of our brain is heavily involved in generating new insights, the full creative process is actually a whole-brain skill. In other words, our creative ability depends on dynamic interactions across a number of different brain regions.[1]

The areas of our brain responsible for creativity have been collectively described as our *imagination network*, a term that was first proposed in 2001. This network largely involves the *frontal, parietal* and *temporal* lobes of our brain.[2]

Creativity lies in the way that all of these lobes interact with each other:

» The **temporal and parietal lobes** store specialised knowledge

» The **frontal lobe** is involved in the development of alternative solutions or perspectives

A recent study using the brain scans of 500 volunteers has also shown that there is a link between our brain structure and creativity.[3]

The findings highlight that those who were more open, creative and receptive to new ideas had a thinner, larger and more wrinkled cortex (outer layer of the brain) compared to the other participants.

The thinner cortex may point to a high level of synaptic pruning, which is a neurological process linked to improved connectivity and cognitive efficiency, as discussed in Chapter 1, Our Brain.

Creativity is messy and contradictory

Today, most psychologists agree that creativity is multifaceted in nature. On a neurological level, creativity is even deemed to be messy. This is because our imagination network is essentially full of contradiction.

On one hand, our imagination network helps us entertain abstract thoughts and allows our mind to wander in time or space. On the other hand, it allows us to focus sharply and deal with the here and now.

In short, the imagination network moves between the rational and the emotional sides of the brain, turning networks on and off.

How are new ideas formed?

When our brain creates anything that is different from what we already know, certain brain regions are activated and work together.

In 2015, a study was carried out at the University of Haifa to examine the creative process in the brain.[4]

Participants were given half a minute to devise a new and original use for different objects. A functional magnetic resonance imaging (fMRI) scanner examined their brain activity while they formulated their idea. The ideas that cropped up less frequently were scored high on originality, while more commonly occurring ideas were given a lower score.

It was found that in the participants who generated the highest degree of originality, brain activity was strong in an area that we use to daydream. In addition to this, another region towards the front of the brain was active – the part that we use for rules and social norms.

The stronger the collaboration between these two brain regions (those responsible for daydreaming and rules/social norms), the higher the level of original thinking.

But too much collaboration can sometimes hinder the creative process. When our brain needs to run totally free and randomly, it cannot be stifled by rules or evaluation. And so it has to switch off the frontal lobe that we use for critical analysis.

Later on, we may consciously activate these frontal lobe regions in order to assess the viability of the ideas that have been generated.

Researchers in California have measured the brain activity of rappers and other musicians whose work involves creative improvisation.[5]

The musicians played a small keyboard while inside a functional magnetic resonance imaging (fMRI) scanner to monitor their brain activity. Through their music, they were asked to convey positive emotions and then negative emotions, and at the same time were shown happy and sad images.

The researchers observed deactivation of the brain's *dorsolateral prefrontal cortex* (DLPFC), which helps to plan and monitor behaviour when conveying positive emotions, suggesting that the musicians were allowing their minds to be unconstrained. When conveying sad emotions, the part of the brain that is linked to reward was activated.

This study highlighted the relationship between creativity and emotion, again proving the involvement of different regions of the brain in the creative process.

Why is a eureka moment never actually out of the blue?

When we experience a sudden insight or moment of inspiration that seems to come to us from nowhere, it is actually the result of different brain regions working together, connecting pieces of information over a period of time.

Although we take information into both our left and right hemispheres, the neurons on our right are wider reaching and can pull in ideas that are further away and unrelated in our brain. Brain studies using electroencephalography (EEG) and functional magnetic resonance imaging (fMRI) show that our brain experiences bursts of high frequency just prior to one of these eureka moments.[6]

In particular, the activation of an area of the brain located in the right hemisphere, known as the *right anterior superior temporal gyrus*, which is involved in musical processing and spatial perception, enables us to connect unrelated objects or concepts.

So if we constantly feed our brain with new information and then allow it to make links and associations, an idea may suddenly come to us when we are least expecting it, or while we are doing something completely unrelated.

Eureka moments

» Microwave

In 1945, Percy Spencer was experimenting with a new vacuum tube when he noticed that the chocolate bar in his pocket was melting. He realised that microwaves being emitted by the vacuum tube could penetrate the exterior of a food and cook it *from the inside out* instead of *from the outside in*. Two years later, the first microwave oven was manufactured, although it was not until 1967 that it was made smaller and more affordable.

» Velcro

In 1948, Swiss engineer George de Mestral went hiking in the woods and noticed that burrs from plants he had walked into had stuck to his clothing. After examining a burr under a microscope and discovering that they were covered in tiny hooks that allowed them to attach to clothes and fur, he created what is now known as Velcro.

» Post-its

In 1968, Spencer Silver at 3M discovered a glue that would not stick. But the company did not pursue the idea until 1974, when another 3M employee, Arthur Fry, used the low-tack glue for bookmarks in his hymn book. Now Post-its are sold all over the world.

» Hypodermic needle

In 2011, scientists in Japan developed a hypodermic needle that is based on a mosquito's proboscis.[7] Instead of being a smooth needle that comes into contact with a considerable amount of skin, causing pain, this new model is serrated and barely touches the skin. The needle mimics the mosquito's mouthparts and breaks the skin in such a way as to reduce the pain normally caused by a syringe – in much the same way as we rarely feel a mosquito bite!

Are creative people different to everyone else?

The question above has been baffling scientists for decades. Just as our creative brain is contradictory and multidirectional, so too it seems that creative people exhibit a range of complex behaviours.

During the 1960s, a series of experiments was conducted on some well-known thinkers of the time to investigate their creativity.[8] Among these thinkers were writers, architects, scientists, entrepreneurs and mathematicians. They were invited to spend time meeting each other and being tested, interviewed and observed. The researchers wanted to assess their personality, mental stability and creativity.

The study found that creativity comprised a range of intellectual, emotional, motivational and moral factors.

What everyone had in common was a willingness to share personal detail, a preference for ambiguity, an unusually high tolerance for disorder, independence and unconventionality, and a willingness to take risks.

To some extent, it does seem that people who spend their time engaged in creative pursuits do stand out from others in a number of aspects: they combine introspection with emotional expression, they are rational and emotional, deliberate and spontaneous, disorderly and organised. These inner conflicts may lead them to create.[9]

In essence, people who are deemed to be creative have allowed themselves to engage in a range of experiences, many of which are reflected in their work. Their heightened sense of self seems to sensitise them to life's ups and downs, and some – such as creative writers – even score high in terms of symptoms of mental illness.

A recent study has considered the creative process by looking at Fields Medallists, Pulitzer Prize winners and six Nobel laureates, examining their personal histories and conducting neuroimaging on their brains.[10]

The study formed the following conclusions:

» Creative people prefer to teach themselves rather than be taught, and they find standard ways of teaching unhelpful.

» Creative people love both the arts and the sciences, while traditional education often encourages a divide between the two.

» Creative people are resilient in the face of scepticism and rejection – although they may suffer anxiety if these factors persist.

This persistence might breed psychological pain, which can manifest as depression or anxiety.

Creative people have bad ideas as well as good ideas. But they may also see connections and possibilities that no one else can see and have the tenacity to try them out.

Nancy Andreasen, who conducted the study, states:

> **'You cannot force creativity to happen – every creative person can attest to that. But the essence of creativity is making connections and solving puzzles.'**

But creativity is also in the small stuff

Being creative does not always have to be linked with great works of art or achievement. We can also be creative with everyday issues, such as how to decorate a table, how to keep children entertained at the weekend, how to present data and how to communicate with the boss.

While many of us have not followed a career path that we would typically associate with creativity, we can nevertheless find a multitude of opportunities to think differently, remove obstacles, see novelty and find possibility in what we do every day.

A number of the greatest inventions have arisen from the ability to imagine another possibility:

» Thomas Edison invented the first multiplex telegraph by observing a water pump.

» Willis Carrier invented the air conditioner after he saw water condensing on the side of a window.

» The physician René Laënnec invented the stethoscope after observing two children sending signals to each other by tapping on a piece of wood with a pin.

'Discovery is seeing what everybody else has seen, and thinking what nobody else has thought.'

Albert Szent-Györgyi

Our senses affect our creativity

Because creativity depends on our ability to make new connections and associations, the more input we receive through our senses, the more material there is for our brain to work with.

People who experience heightened sensory input and an intermingling of the senses may have hyperconnectivity of certain brain regions. This is a condition called *synaesthesia*, which affects one in 2,000 people. Synaesthetes may experience conjoined sensory input, such as seeing numbers in different colours, or tasting strawberries when they hear the word 'book'.

The symptoms of synaesthesia are considered to be genetic, although other researchers have suggested that the condition is a result of earlier pruning issues in the brain. It has been found to be more common in artists, poets and writers, leading researchers to make the association between synaesthesia with high brain interconnectivity and creativity.[11]

Sight: Daylight has a better impact on our cognitive performance than artificial light,[12] but dim lighting can enhance our creative performance.[13]

Smell: Smell is a powerful enhancer of emotion and brain agility:[14]

» Lemon and jasmine can improve cognitive functioning.
» Vanilla and cinnamon can help enhance creativity.
» Rosemary and grapefruit are energising and stimulating.

Sound: Focus sometimes does require silence and freedom from any distraction, but a moderate level of ambient noise (such as background conversation) can also sometimes boost our creative powers.[15]

Taste: Fresh fruit and vegetables can stimulate positive changes in mood and are effective fuel for creative thinking.[16]

Touch: Temperature impacts cognitive performance. A warmer workspace is more conducive to cognitive efficiency than a cold one. When our workspace is too cold, we are using our energy and resources in trying to stay warm, and we make more errors.[17] This is explained further in Chapter 11, Our Brain and Leadership.

Is intelligence linked to creativity?

Intelligence can be summarised as our capacity for learning, reasoning and understanding.

Some researchers believe that there is a positive relationship between intelligence and creativity. It makes sense that intelligence and the ability to store more information may then provide more for the brain to work with and connect – thereby becoming more creative.

The *Threshold Theory*[18] suggests that highly creative people have an intelligence quotient (IQ) of about 120 (see Figure 8.2 for ranges).

IQ Range	Classification
Above 145	Genius or near genius
130–144	Very superior
115–129	Superior
85–114	Normal

Figure 8.2: IQ ranges

With anything that is above that, the relationship between IQ and creativity is not as evident. This may suggest that a very high IQ may not necessarily mean high creativity.[19]

Part 2: Impact on our daily life

Can we learn to be creative?

The short answer to the question above is yes! Creativity is not a fixed ability that we are born with. It emerges through a number of processes that lead to new ways of thinking.

But many of us need to train our minds to produce new ideas. In order to do this, we have to rethink our view of creativity as being due purely to genius and instead see it as a thinking skill that we can all learn.

And so creativity is less about *who people are* and more about *what people do*. When we accept this we are able to allow our brains to enjoy the creative process as much as those whom we consider to be truly creative.

We can all boost our creativity by consciously deciding to engage in cognitive techniques that stretch our thinking.[20]

Creative skill		Creative action
Connection		Allow random thoughts and ideas to enter your mind and your brain will start to piece them together. We need to see connections and relationships between different facts, ideas or existing components.
Daydreaming		Give your brain time and space to think, reflect and entertain abstact thought. Find creative space. When we daydream and relax, our alpha brainwaves are prominent and sensory input is minimised. This state is called *optimal inattention* and is also achieved during meditation and mindfulness.
Shifting		Break away from your work for five minutes and generate as many ideas as possible on your own (e.g. find different words to rename something). This is a more effective way of producing different ideas than brainstorming, which has limited value because of the power of *groupthink* or collective judgement. Groups are better at idea selection than idea creation.
Thinking like a child		We need to combine work and play. Experiment – without judgement or criticism. Our brain works best when it is relaxed, happy and free to explore possibilities.
Persistence		We need to motivate ourselves to try, endure failure and try again. As Tom Peters said, we need to 'Fail Fast – Learn Fast – Fix Fast'.
Using our nose		Of all of our senses, our sense of smell provides the most powerful link to memory. This phenomenon, known as the Proust effect, can often trigger lost memories and emotions from the past to inspire and create new ideas.

Figure 8.3: Cognitive techniques that boost creativity

The actor and comedian John Cleese describes our brain as being like a tortoise: a tortoise pokes its head out to check that the environment is safe before it fully emerges. For creativity to take hold, we therefore need to create a safe place like a tortoise's shell.

Creativity will only emerge when it feels that the time is right and that it will not be threatened by other thoughts.

Creativity is not fragile: we need to challenge it!

We need to work on our ideas, test them and even criticise them. Our ideas can handle it! Ideas need work, scrutiny, judgement and expansion. In allowing ourselves to work on an idea, we may find ourselves discovering different dimensions and possibilities. We should not treat ideas as if they were fragile.

Overcoming challenges can create the right conditions for creativity to flourish. Failure can ignite the creative regions of the brain and we will then try even harder to compensate for not succeeding the first time.

Convergent versus divergent thinking

Creativity needs us to think *divergently* rather than *convergently*. However, as humans we are more convergent than divergent thinkers.

449 Failures!

In the 1960s, Unilever – a company known for manufacturing laundry detergent – had a major problem. The nozzle that they used to turn chemicals into a powder kept blocking.

Unilever's mathematicians could not fix the problem.

Finally, Unilever asked their biologists who, using a different, evolutionary-based approach, made a series of smaller incremental adjustments. After 45 different models and 449 failures they created a nozzle that worked.[21]

And Dyson failed over 5,000 times!

Thirty years ago James Dyson imagined redesigning the vacuum cleaner. Frustrated with how the vacuum bag clogged with dust, he decided to replace it with a fast-spinning motor that created a cyclone of air that, in turn, created suction.

Some 5,127 designs later, Dyson's first vacuum cleaner was rejected by British retailers. The first models were sold only in Japan, where they were very successful. By the mid-90s Dyson's vacuum cleaner had become a bestseller in the United Kingdom. As James Dyson says:

> 'We fail every day. Failure is the best medicine – as long as you learn something.'

Convergent thinking is mainly focused on providing the right answer or solution, rather than on how to solve a problem. We effectively *converge* on the best approach and address any deviation from the correct path. Convergent thinking relies on plans and logic. Most corporate strategies are developed from convergent thinking.

Divergent thinking looks for alternatives and widens our spectrum of available ideas. Divergent thinking opens up our thinking to consider arbitrary concepts. It feels more chaotic and disorganised but it is often the source of additional ideas. Divergent thinking enables us to consider unusual combinations and multiple possibilities. It tests notions and sees where they take us.

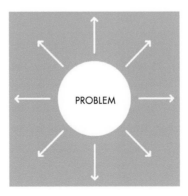

Twitter is a result of divergent thinking. When Twitter was developed it did not have an obvious practical application. There was no clear underpinning strategy or formula for success.

Twitter was launched to see what the take-up would be. The aim was to refine the application only after determining how many people used it.

After testing the market and seeing where the idea could go, Twitter has gone on to become one of the world's most popular and widely used social networking services.

Nevertheless, there is a role for convergent thinking. When divergent thinking has exhausted all random ideas and connections, then ideas need to be narrowed down and selected. This is when we can apply convergent thinking.

But we should guard against moving too quickly into convergent thinking simply because we need quick answers *now*. Ideas need to be worked on, connected, challenged and tested. This can take time.

Why do many of us stop being creative?

As will be discussed in Chapter 12, Our Brain and Lifestyle, our brain is a muscle, and the more we use it, the fitter and stronger it becomes. Creativity is a brain skill that many of us have stopped using; consequently, we believe that we are not creative.

The difference between people who are creative and those who think they are not creative is that creative people have not given up and stopped using their imagination.

We can all generate original ideas, but often we do not allow these ideas to take hold. We convince ourselves either that we are too busy or that our idea is worthless. And when the ideas we put forward are rejected or overlooked, we revert to behaviour that is more successful, which often means quick answers that have obvious benefits. This weakens our creative connections over time.

Having to be practical can also be an obstruction to the creative process. We spend so much of our time focusing on relevance and application that we do not value the more abstract exercise of simply letting our minds wander.

We first need to let our mind explore what is possible before determining its pragmatic benefit. Creativity needs to be able to flow naturally without the boundaries of time and the pressures of problem-solving.

Why does brainstorming not always work?

Concepts such as brainstorming are designed to facilitate a broader way of thinking, but the very process is often constricted by having to think about a specific solution.

When we are under pressure to brainstorm ideas for a solution, we are not relaxed. Our brain does not respond creatively to this forced method of idea generation. If we want to get the best out of the creative process we need to minimise anxiety and relax our brain.

We also need to be away from the judgment of others. Group brainstorming can sometimes turn into an ideas-critiquing session, which defeats its purpose. We have much better ideas when we are free to explore any possibility, however crazy it may seem. It may just lead us to the right solution.

As explained earlier in this chapter, groups are better at idea selection than idea creation.

How we crush creativity early on

One of the most watched TED talks of all time is by Sir Ken Robinson, an author, speaker and international advisor on education. Sir Ken decries the lack of creative opportunities for children in education and describes research highlighting how divergent thinking falls away as we get older. He claims that:

> ### 'We are educating people out of their creative capacities.'

Sir Ken describes creativity as the *genetic code of education*, citing it as a critical tool in modern life.

If we look at young children, we can see that they are naturally creative. They explore, experiment, laugh and have fun while they are coming up with new ideas. But, by the time children are ready to move to secondary school, this creative spark has all too often been extinguished.

Creativity needs freedom: freedom to play, freedom to think, freedom to draw, freedom to imagine. This is equally true of the adult world, but the creative freedom that is present in the young child is all too often crushed by an environment of over-control, over-measurement and over-reward.

Our early years of divergent thinking are instructed out of us as education systems give us fewer options, reduce our horizons and teach us to converge on one correct answer.

While 84% of children are creative when they start their kindergarten years, by the time they are six or seven years old only 10% have remained creative.[22]

By the time we are 25, only 2% of us are still creative.

The other issue is that children today have never been busier: their after-school schedules are crammed with activities and they have no room in their lives to create on their own.

Feeling bored is good for children because they explore ways to reduce their boredom. They also learn to be intrinsically motivated and driven less by external rewards and more by the joy they find in doing something for themselves.

The biggest problem we all have is our overreliance on technology and the sedentary lifestyles many of us now lead. Our addiction to our electronic devices means that we are not physically mobile, and when our body is still then our brain activity drops.

Children will regain their natural creativity and curiosity by being encouraged to run around and play. Not only will their brains will love it, their bodies will too!

Reigniting and harnessing the creative spark

If our creative spark is to be reignited and harnessed by educators, leaders, policy-makers and parents, some attention needs to be paid to the conditions under which we expect people to thrive.

But while many enterprises expound the need for creativity in their people, they find themselves caught up in the dilemma of whether to increase efficiency and raise productivity or encourage the complex, unpredictable and messy exploration of ideas. The question is: are both of these activities possible at the same time? When times are tough, is room created for the free flow of ideas, or is emphasis placed instead on cost-cutting and the removal of anything that is non-essential to the bottom line?

A great deal of research has been carried out over the years to assess the relationship between creativity or *innovation* (which is a creative idea that has been turned into a replicable product or service that satisfies a specific need) with managing for profitable growth. Few organisations, it seems, have been able to master the two disciplines concurrently.

One notable exception is the software company the SAS Institute, which regularly features in *Fortune*'s 100 Best Companies to Work For list.[23] In the 2017 list *Fortune* cites one SAS employee as saying:

'They simply want to make life easy and carefree for us because that's the key to innovation.'

SAS believes that employees do their best when they are intellectually engaged and free from distractions like day-care, healthcare and dry-cleaning, which are all provided on site. There is no distinction between the *creative* people and *non-creative* people: *everyone is creative*. Even the CEO still writes code. Managers are responsible for promoting and fostering the right environment for creative thinking and for ensuring that people take regular breaks. Long hours are frowned upon. People are trusted to manage their own workload and experiment in a spirit of collaboration. Moreover, the organisation has consistently enjoyed revenue growth.

Creativity is inconvenient and often disruptive. It gets in the way of our day-to-day work and interrupts our established methods and processes. To harness creativity means to let go of old ideas, systems and methods – a concept that is hard to practise in most organisations. And the fact that organisations like SAS are outside the norm, means that the majority of us do not benefit from environments that encourage freedom of expression, tolerance of failure and enthusiasm for learning.

We still have a long way to go before organisations universally embrace a creative paradigm and allow for the genesis and nourishment of ideas on a continual and often chaotic basis.

Why are bad ideas still good ideas?

Having many bad ideas also means we will have a lot of good ideas! The trick is to keep having ideas – and enjoy the process while it is happening. Creativity thrives in a fun atmosphere where we turn normal thinking on its head.

When we feel that we are only allowed to have good ideas, we often block our creative flow and deny ourselves any ideas that we think may be considered not good.

Creativity needs space, practice and exercise. We need to exercise our creative muscle. The more ideas we have, the better they will become. Sometimes bad ideas turn into good ideas – or at least a bad idea may sow the seeds for a good idea to grow.

'Every day I write down ideas.

I write down so many ideas that it hurts my head to come up with one more. Then I try to write down five more.

The other day I tried to write 100 alternatives kids can do other than go to college. I wrote down eight, which I wrote about here. I couldn't come up with any more.

Then the next day I came up with another 40. It definitely stretched my head.'

James Altucher[24]
(investor, writer and entrepreneur)

Deliberately generating bad ideas allows people to engage in an unfettered form of reverse brainstorming. Bad ideas can then be reversed, in order to see whether the opposite idea may lead somewhere.

'Alice laughed: "There's no use trying," she said; "one can't believe impossible things."

"I daresay you haven't had much practice," said the Queen. "When I was younger, I always did it for half an hour a day. Why, sometimes I've believed as many as six impossible things before breakfast."'

Lewis Carroll

Green is good for creativity

A number of recent studies have explored how exposure to green space can boost creativity and cognitive skills. In Spain, an association has been established between green surroundings and measures of cognitive development in 2,593 primary schoolchildren aged between seven and ten years.[25]

Green scenes can also have a restorative effect on our brain and boost our concentration. A study involving 150 students has shown how the brain is stimulated and enhanced by a short view of a flowering green meadow compared to a bare concrete roof.[26]

The same study also emphasised the importance of short mental breaks for our ability to focus and reactivate our brain. Just a 40-second intermission, to reset our thinking about the task in hand, can make a considerable difference to our cognitive performance.

Part 3: Stories and top tips

Sleepiness removes constraints . . .

To create his surreal paintings, Salvador Dalí experimented with the time period between sleep and wakefulness. This period is when different sensations and perceptions from the day appear to us as *hypnagogic* images (the word *hypnagogic* comes from the Greek for 'leading to sleep') or light dreams and abstract thoughts.

Dalí wanted to capture these for his paintings.

One of the techniques he used was to sit beside a tin plate on the floor while he held a spoon in his hand over the plate. As he relaxed or fell asleep, the spoon would fall from his fingers and on to the plate and wake him up. During the ensuing hypnagogic period, images would connect with other completely unrelated images in Dalí's brain – and these are what he painted.

When we are awake, we rely on known connections, but as we enter sleep, our brain is able to be freer and make new and different associations.

. . . but sometimes constraint is good

In 1960, the publishing company Random House bet an author $50 that he would not be able to write a children's book in fewer than 50 words. The author accepted the bet and won it. The book was *Green Eggs and Ham* and the author was Dr Seuss.

Green Eggs and Ham is one of the best-selling children's books in history and has sold over 200 million copies.

Dr Seuss's creativity was ignited because of the 50-word limit. It was so successful that he applied the same strategy to *The Cat in the Hat*, using a vocabulary list of only 236 very simple words.

Limits and boundaries can help the creative process by forcing us to find solutions that may otherwise not have occurred to us; we seek ways of making something work within given restrictions. Our brain loves a challenge!

Do the opposite to what people expect

Apple's first Macintosh commercial, directed by Ridley Scott (who had already directed *Blade Runner* and *Alien* and went on to direct *Thelma and Louise, Gladiator* and a number of other high-profile films), is a powerful example of how to challenge accepted and expected norms. Designed to be disruptive and to jolt people out of what they were used to, the commercial contrasted the newcomer Apple with the existing world of computing, dominated at that time by IBM. The result was ground-breaking.

Both Apple's commercial and computer represented something completely different. The Macintosh computer was the first personal computer to include a graphical-user interface and its ease of use appealed to the less technologically savvy, as well as those who wanted to be at the edge of innovation.

Innovator or fast follower?

Recent research suggests that those we often label pioneers have, in reality, been fast followers. It is very difficult to enter a brand-new market or present a brand-new product. The failure rate is high. A more strategically sound approach may be to exploit what is already out there and then adjust it for greater success.

For example, many of Apple's remarkable achievements lie not in an ability to innovate in the pure sense of the word, but in the skill of improving products already on the market. The iPod was not the first MP3 player, but it was viewed as being better than existing devices because it was priced and sized differently, with the added benefit of the iTunes service. And every year, iPads and iPhones slim down or shape up, offering better screens and faster systems. The key, it seems, is to follow the competition, faster and better than before.

In the words of the Scottish–American industrialist, Andrew Carnegie:

'It is better to be a follower
than a pioneer.
The pioneers get scalped.'

Inspire yourself by looking at the world around you. Make connections and think of possibilities using random objects and ideas. The next good idea is often found in the unlikeliest place. Let your mind run free.

Disrupt your habitual thought patterns. Do the opposite of what you would normally do. Give your brain a jolt! Criticise your own ideas and give them a workout. Think of bad ideas as well as good ideas. Sometimes a bad idea reversed can become a very good idea!

Enjoy abstract thoughts, especially when you feel tired. Sometimes creative ideas come when your brain is not trying to compete with other pressures and thoughts. When our brain is relaxed, ideas will often come to us.

Allow your mind to wander and daydream. Imagine 'what if?' or 'why not?' This will activate your imagination network. Build on other people's ideas and let the process develop organically. Support and build on other people's creative suggestions. Sometimes it is the second person to speak that determines the fate of any idea.

Sleep on a problem. If you cannot find a solution, relax and let sleep go to work on it for you. You may find that you have the answer in the morning. Your brain will be more creative when it is relaxed.

References for Chapter 8

1 Gregoire, C. & S.B. Kaufman (2016) *Wired to Create: Unraveling the Mysteries of the Creative Mind*. New York: TarcherPerigee

2 Raichle, M. et al. (2001) 'A default mode of brain function', *PNAS*, January, 676–82

3 Riccelli, R. et al. (2017) 'Surface-based morphometry reveals the neuroanatomical basis of the five-factor model of personality', *Social Cognitive and Affective Neuroscience*, April, 671–84

4 Mayseless, N. et al. (2015) 'How does our brain form creative and original ideas?', *Science Daily*, 19 November [www.sciencedaily.com/releases/2015/11/151119104105.htm]

5 Limb, C. et al. (2016) 'Emotional intent modulates the neural substrates of creativity: an fMRI study of emotionally targeted improvisation in jazz musicians', *Scientific Reports*, January [doi.org/10.1038/srep18460]

6 Kounios, J. & M. Beeman (2014) 'The cognitive neuroscience of insight', *Annual Review of Psychology*, 65 and 71–93

7 Izumi H. et al. (2011). 'Realistic imitation of mosquito's proboscis: electrochemically etched sharp and jagged needles and the cooperative inserting motion', *Sensor and Actuators: A Physical Journal*, January, 115–23

8 Barron, F. (1963) *Creativity and Psychological Health: Origins of Personality and Creative Freedom*. Princeton, NJ: Van Nostrand

9 Csikszentmihalyi, M. (1996) *Creativity: Flow and the Psychology of Discovery and Invention*, New York: HarperCollins

10 Andreasen, N. (2014) 'Secrets of the creative brain', *The Atlantic*, July–August, 15–20

11 Ramachandran, V.S. & D. Brang (2011) 'Survival of the synesthesia gene: why do people hear colors and taste words', *PLOS Biology*, 22 November [doi.org/10.1371/journal.pbio.1001205]

12 Münch, M. et al. (2012) 'Effects of prior light exposure on early evening performance, subjective sleepiness, and hormonal secretion', *Behavioral Neuroscience*, February, 196–203

13 Steidle, A. & L. Werth (2013) 'Freedom from constraints: darkness and dim illumination promote creativity', *Journal of Environmental Psychology*, September, 67–80

14 Augustin, S. (2009) 'The smell is right – using scents to enhance life', *Psychology Today*, 23 December [psychologytoday.com]

15 Mehta, R. et al. (2012) 'Is noise always bad? Exploring the effects of ambient noise on creative cognition', *Journal of Consumer Research*, December, 784–99

16 Conner, T.S. et al. (2017) 'Let them eat fruit! The effect of fruit and vegetable consumption on psychological well-being in young adults: A randomized controlled trial', *PLOS ONE*, 3 February [doi/org/10.1371/journal.pone.0171206]

17 Hedge, A. (2005) 'Thermal effects on office productivity', *Proceedings of the Human Factors and Ergonomics Society Annual Meeting*, September, 823–27

18 Torrance E.P. (1966) *Torrance Tests of Creative Thinking: Norms and Technical Manual-Research Edition*, Princeton, NJ: Personnel Press

19 Jauk, E. et al. (2013) 'The relationship between intelligence and creativity', *Intelligence*, July, 212–21

20 Epstein, R. (2016) 'How to enhance the creativity of a person and figuring out the mysteries of the creative process', *Psychology Today*, 9 June [psychologytoday.com]

21 Syed, M. (2015) *Black Box Thinking: Marginal Gains and the Secrets of High Performance*. London: John Murray

22 McGarvey, R. (1990) Creative Thinking, *USAIR*, June, 36

23 Florida, R. & J. Goodnight (2005) 'Managing for creativity', *Harvard Business Review*, July–August, 124–31

24 Altucher, J. (2011) 'How to be THE LUCKIEST GUY ON THE PLANET in 4 easy steps', *Business Insider*, 25 February [businessinsider.com]

25 Dadvand, P. et al. (2015) 'Green spaces and cognitive development in primary schoolchildren', *PNAS*, June, 7937–42

26 Lee, K.E. et al. (2015) '40-second green roof views sustain attention: The role of micro-breaks in attention restoration', *Journal of Environmental Psychology*, June, 182–89

'Progress is impossible without change and those who cannot change their minds cannot change anything.'

George Bernard Shaw

Playwright and socialist
(1856–1950)

9: OUR BRAIN AND CHANGE

About this chapter

The world is changing faster than ever. *New* is everywhere: new technologies, new devices, new possibilities, new demands – effectively new ways of living, learning and working.

But most of us do not like change. We find comfort in routines, habits and what feels familiar. Even the changes that we choose for ourselves pose some difficulty and need readjustment. Although most of us accept that competitive advantage depends on our ability to adapt quickly, change is not a phenomenon that we readily embrace.

This chapter considers what change means both for individuals and for organisations. It offers insights into how habits are formed and changed, what is needed to help people manage change in themselves and others, and why resilience is a vital ingredient in our increasingly turbulent world.

A better understanding of how our brain handles change will help us to handle the unexpected and unpredictable around us.

Part 1: The science explained

Change is painful for the brain

We naturally resist change because change represents uncertainty – and uncertainty is threatening and painful for a brain that wants to keep us safe and alive. Although many of today's threats are no longer life-or-death situations, our brain still protects us as if they were just that.

Figure 9.1: Change is pain in the brain

A threat does not even need to be a real one; it is how we view the threat that affects the way our brain responds to it. Psychological pain and physical pain are registered in our brain in exactly the same way.[1] This is further highlighted in Chapter 11, Our Brain and Leadership.

When we feel uncertain or anxious, our fight-or-flight mechanisms are mobilised. Resources are diverted from our *frontal lobe* and we focus instead on survival. When this happens, there is increased activity in 1) the *anterior cingulate cortex* (worry), 2) the *orbital frontal cortex* (error prediction), 3) the *insula* (pain and disgust) and 4) the *amygdala* (anxiety).

As soon as these four regions of the brain are engaged, resources are diverted from the frontal lobe area, which we use for higher-level intellectual functioning, and become focused instead on survival.

Our capacity for rational thought is thus diminished, and even when the change is a good idea we still resist it.

In studies of patients who have undergone heart bypass surgery, only one in nine people, on average, adopts healthier habits to prevent a relapse.

Our response to change may be summarised as follows:

Change (uncertainty)

Threat response (fight or flight)

Increased anxiety and fear

Reduced ability to focus and think clearly

Impaired performance and increased emotion

Anxiety is contagious

As explained in Chapter 7, Our Brain and Biases, we do a great deal to avoid loss. When we think we are at risk of loss – loss of our job, loss of the skill we have spent years mastering, loss of our reputation – we become anxious. And when we are anxious, it spreads like a contagion across our social groups.

Recent Gallup analysis highlights the finding that the wellbeing of leaders and the wellbeing of their teams are interdependent.[2] The emotional state of each affects the emotional state of the other.

In times of change, therefore, our anxious state can influence and exacerbate the states of those around us. This can even lead to a heightened pattern of thought, known as *cognitive vulnerability*, which is also contagious.

College students were randomly assigned to a roommate. The higher the level of cognitive vulnerability in one of the students, the more likely the other was to develop higher levels of cognitive vulnerability. The students whose cognitive vulnerability increased also later showed higher levels of depressive symptoms.[3]

Why do our brains love routine and habits?

Our routine activities use an area of the brain with a group of neurons in the temporal lobe called the *basal ganglia* (see Figure 9.2), which play a significant role in the formation of long-standing habits. The basal ganglia are activated by familiar and repetitive activity to which we no longer have to pay attention.

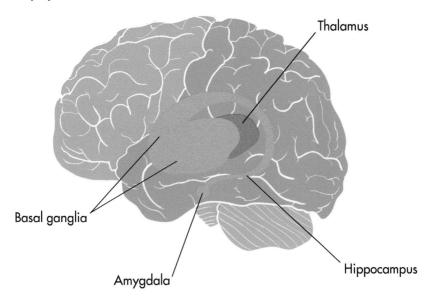

Figure 9.2: The basal ganglia

This area of the brain requires much less energy than our working memory (which is what we use to pay attention to new information) because it uses brain circuits that have already been shaped and defined by experience.

All activities that are repeated eventually become orchestrated by the basal ganglia, thereby freeing up the prefrontal cortex to focus on fresh inputs.

Practice and routine therefore become hard-wired into our brain and any habit, good or bad, is hard for our brain to override. Although bad habits often linger in the brain, it is possible to override them over time with good habits that are more powerful.

Experience and expectation are interlinked

Because we are constantly using previously stored knowledge to help us deal with new information, as has been explained in other chapters, our expectations will therefore generally drive our experiences.

This is particularly true of pain and pain relief, which is why the *placebo effect* is so powerful. This effect, whereby an inactive substance like sugar or distilled water can sometimes improve a patient's condition simply because the patient expects to benefit, has been shown to have the ability to improve our breathing (our lungs dilate), heal ulcers and reduce blood pressure.

However, the reverse of this is more negative. When it comes to pain itself, we often experience more pain when we expect in advance that something will be painful. This is called the *nocebo effect*. The suggestion of pain is enough to stimulate the experience of pain, which is why doctors and dentists need to be cognisant of the language they use with patients, as discussed in Chapter 5, Our Brain and Language.

Our expectation of a new change initiative is often coloured by a bad or difficult experience of previous change. Our sensitivity to the pain of the change is intensified accordingly. Similarly, if we expect a change programme to be positive we will actually increase its likelihood of success.

So when we repeatedly focus on something being either painful or pain-free, our neural circuits will strengthen in either direction. We can increase or decrease our own discomfort, depending on where we choose to direct our thoughts.

> A study found that people's expectations of less pain brought about a reduction of 28.4% in perceived pain.[4] This result was comparable to the effects of an actual drug, morphine.

When we expect pain to be lower, we will therefore perceive it as lower, but the experience of what is painful seems to be slightly different for men and women.[5] Studies have found that male participants are able to endure pain for longer than female participants, and that women are more willing to report pain than men are.

This has significant implications in a changing environment where leaders need to stay abreast of any issues among the individuals involved. If the environment is male-dominated, for example, there may be a higher degree of silent acceptance and stoicism, which may not be helpful in the long term.

Part 2: Impact on our daily life

Why do most change efforts in organisations fail?

Most leaders do not fully understand the impact of change on their people. Many change efforts fail because people's need for certainty is not properly addressed by the provision of adequate information for the duration of a change initiative. Communication can be spurious or concerned solely with hard facts and logic, while the emotional aspects of the change are often dismissed or completely overlooked. All too frequently, any change-related messages are posted on an intranet portal with the expectation that everyone will automatically read and understand them.

Change is difficult because it effectively means a rewiring of our brain, and this cannot happen overnight. To effect real change, leaders need to be supportive and, above all, exercise patience and understanding. Change therefore takes time.

Leaders regularly underestimate the pain that is being experienced throughout an organisation because their vantage point is different. Not surprisingly, the implementation and assimilation of new practices and routines are not straightforward at all.

Successful change needs the right leadership

The success of any change initiative largely depends on how much energy and enthusiasm is demonstrated by leaders. So much has already been published about the leader's role during change, yet still this continues to be a real issue.

Leaders often miss emotional signs of resistance or distress because they are so focused on polished presentations and correct messaging. And they do not have the time to devote to dealing with personal concerns and individual issues.

But our natural negativity bias ensures that negative emotions spread far more quickly than positive emotions, which means that leadership effort must be dedicated to dealing with this fallout. And so the best gift leaders can give to their people is their time. Listening is crucial – and when people feel that they are being heard, then they are more likely to listen in return.

As well as engaging in listening, leaders also need to put thought into the language they use with the people around them. The more positive and encouraging the language, and the greater the focus on team effort and collaboration, the more our reward network is activated, spurring us on to greater endeavour. There are certain words to which our brain responds positively or negatively – a topic that was explored in more depth in Chapter 5, Our Brain and Language.

Leading change: dealing with the push-back first

When we tell our brain what to do, it automatically resists and behaves just like a naughty child. As Newton's third law states:

'For every action, there is an equal and opposite reaction.'

Resistance may also be explained by our brain's desire to achieve balance, or *homeostasis*.

Leaders need to recognise the power of the *push-back* from employees when any change initiative is first announced, as well as later, during the various forms and methods of communication that occur.

This push-back is highlighted in a useful model called *Force Field Analysis*, which illustrates how resisting forces (people's worries, anxieties and emotions) will arise for every driving force (reasons for the change, such as improved efficiency, reduced headcount, automation of certain processes):

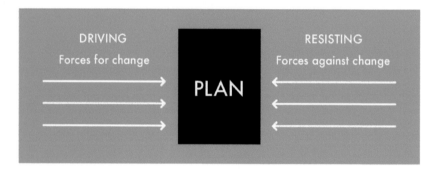

Figure 9.3: Force Field Analysis

Unless the resisting forces are first defused, before time and resources are spent pushing the driving forces on to people, the planned change will never fully achieve its desired outcome.

Resisting forces are also weakened when there is better communication, consultation and listening. Chapter 11, Our Brain and Leadership, considers the role of leadership in keeping people motivated and focused. During times of change, this leadership role is even more critical.

We like the challenge of change – if we are given enough freedom

William Glasser states that we are genetically driven to satisfy our basic needs of survival, love and belonging, power, freedom and fun.[6]

Having the freedom to think, develop our own insights and make our own choices will activate our reward network and enhance our personal satisfaction. We are then motivated to repeat this experience, so change can therefore become a series of sequential, energising activities.

Feelings of achievement will then prevent the brain from resisting change and nullify the effect of the amygdala's threat response. We accept and support something much more if we have chosen it ourselves.

When we make our own choices, we are motivated intrinsically and find pleasure in what we do. *Intrinsic motivation* relies on autonomy, but granting this autonomy is often a challenge for leaders, whose job it is to set the direction and distribute the work.

The good news is that we only need to *feel* that we have a choice in order to ignite our intrinsic motivation. And in any

Explain the *why*

Leaders do not need to focus on the *what*. The *why* is enough to give us a sense of purpose and direction. We can then work out the *how* for ourselves.

Test ideas and solutions

Leaders can involve their teams in generating ideas and solutions, and then in the testing of these. When we feel part of any solution, we are more likely to contribute towards its implementation.

case, leaders can do a great deal to provide their people with opportunities to make choices within the parameters of the business goals.

We need other people around us

We are social beings. In our modern world, which has been dehumanised to a large extent by technology, our fundamental need for closeness to and acceptance by others is stronger than ever.

During times of change and uncertainty, our social networks are an important source of reassurance and comfort, but becoming attuned to the mental and emotional state of others relies on personal rather than virtual contact. It is only when we spend time with people that we can pick up emotional cues that may otherwise have gone undetected. This is true of all age groups.

A study has shown that even the younger generation who have grown up in the digital age need real people.[7]

Eleven-year-olds were divided into two groups:

Group 1 experienced a normal week with access to computers.

Group 2 went to a nature/science camp with no access to computers for a week. The children had to spend their time interacting with each other and with the adults at the camp.

At the end of the week the children at the camp (Group 2) were able to detect emotions more accurately and read people more accurately than Group 1 could.

And so even in a world where the new normal is constant access to technology, we cannot deny our instinctive need to bond with others on an emotional level.

Information is essential during change initiatives

Although this book has made positive reference to Apple in the context of creativity, there is nevertheless a dark aspect to the way the majority of Apple employees work: secrecy.

Much has been made of Steve Jobs's method of guarding the detail of a new product until the moment of its unveiling. An article on 22 June 2009 in the *New York Times* describes how Apple's secrecy even extended to Jobs's own health problems.

But while Apple's clandestine culture has become an effective marketing ploy that thrills customers and delights investors, it is not a strategy that works well for most of us. Our brain responds well to transparency and has a strong need to feel informed, involved and included.

We crave certainty and, as soon as we get it, we activate our brain's reward centre, releasing the neurotransmitter *dopamine*. As Chapter 1, Our Brain, explains, dopamine is associated with a number of brain functions such as learning, working memory and voluntary movement. Dopamine is also our *motivation molecule* and is fired in anticipation of reward. In other words, dopamine mobilises us to act – and it makes us feel good.

Information gives us certainty – and any information is better than no information. When our brain receives information, especially after a period of uncertainty, we stop worrying and instead find that we have more energy and drive.

We also like to see the whole picture – the context. When we cannot see the whole picture, we start to feel uncertain and anxious and we do whatever we can to fill in the missing parts. This is why there is so much misinformation when a situation is ambiguous. If we do not receive sufficient amounts of the right information, we supplement what we do get with our own assumptions, opinions and interpretations.

> The way anxiety can be manipulated has been researched for decades.
>
> A study has shown that, when we anticipate an event that is unpredictable and therefore threatening, our experience of pain is enhanced.[8]

Information is therefore critical during periods of change. The more people are consulted and informed, the greater the reduction in their anxiety levels – and the more accurately messages are circulated.

Change can be good for our brain

Our brain's plasticity means that it will adapt to new activities or routines over time and it will reshape and reorganise itself accordingly.

Change can therefore stimulate our brain in the right way. When we decide to change and make an effort to learn something new and then stick at it, our brain starts to change. It literally rewires itself.

Habits mean that our brain has made certain cognitive processes automatic. We are creatures of routine: we stick to what we know because it feels comfortable and safe. Chapters 3 and 4, on memory and attention, have discussed what happens when our behaviour becomes hard-wired into the neural structure of our brain.

When we practise new behaviours and activities, our brain adapts by creating new neural pathways over time. This is how our brain hard-wires a new habit.

 New behaviours also need to become rooted in the norms and values of an organisation, whereupon they become an embedded part of the new culture. When leaders try to lead change, they often overlook the hard-wiring of existing habits and the fact that it will take time for people to learn how to rewire new habits into their brain.

We need to stay fit and healthy

Change can be exhausting and depletes our resources. It is even more important during these periods of change that we focus on our physical health and maintain an upbeat mood when times feel challenging.

Sleep and exercise are particularly important for our brain, since they help to maintain healthy cognitive function and also keep the body in balance. This will be covered in Chapter 12, Our Brain and Lifestyle.

Resilience is key

Resilience is our ability to recover or bounce back from a difficulty or challenge. Resilience has been a topic of research since the 1960s and it continues to be an area of interest in a number of different contexts.

We love stories of resilience – such as J.K. Rowling's remarkable ability to write her first Harry Potter book while struggling financially and then to cope with multiple rejections before her eventual publication and worldwide success.

Resilience is very personal and can vary from situation to situation. It is a significant aspect of how an individual will deal with change, and for this reason it is becoming an increasingly important ingredient in organisational success.

Psychologists believe that, while it seems that some people are naturally more resilient than others, we can nevertheless learn to develop resilience over our lifetime.

Much of a resilient mind-set stems from being able to view the world through a positive lens and cope with setbacks and adversity. Resilience is also bolstered by an ability to find solutions as problems arise, and to view even the most difficult situations as opportunities to learn and grow.

Endorphins are critical to a resilient system and these are released when we exercise and laugh. Endorphins diminish the perception of pain and reduce anxiety. They are discussed in more detail in Chapter 2, Our Brain and Emotion.

Create the right conditions for change

The power of the *push-back,* or resisting forces, during times of change means that we are not good at being told what to do. A more effective technique is to encourage people to make changes for themselves by fostering the right conditions for these changes to take place.

Robert Cialdini's work on persuasion and influence highlights six principles that drive any new behaviour:[9]

Reciprocity

We will respond to people who do us a favour. When this favour is unexpected, it is even more powerful. John McFarlane, former CEO of ANZ Bank, sent a bottle of champagne to every employee at Christmas with a card thanking them for their work on the company's *Perform, Grow and Break-out* change programme. Rewards have a disproportionately positive impact on change motivation and often the effect will last for months, if not years.

Social Proof

Sometimes we just need to see what other people have done first. Amazon, for example, does this effectively by showing us what choices other people have made. We look to others, especially when we feel uncertain ourselves. This is why all change initiatives need *early adopters* and small successes at the beginning – to help to convince others.

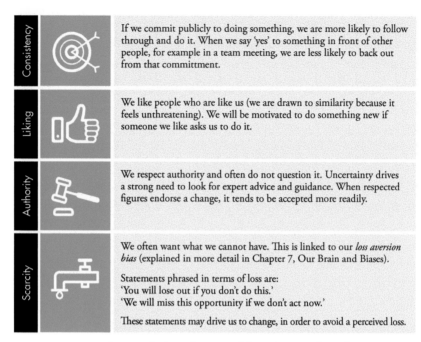

Figure 9.4: Robert Cialdini's Principles of Persuasion

Part 3: Stories and top tips

We need to change, even when life is good!

Change does not occur solely in response to a crisis. Those organisations that enable both continuous reflection and improvement, even when business is good, and take frequent adaptive measures to help meet shifting challenges, are often the most successful.

One of the worst phrases we can use is 'Why fix it if it ain't broke?', which implies that we need to wait for something to break before we address it.

The key to managing ongoing regular changes – both big and small – is a dynamic and agile culture whereby business models and strategies are revisited, reviewed and revised as circumstances change.

All this requires an ability to read early warning signals and respond rapidly. New ideas are the currency of the future. But in order to generate new ideas, many organisations will need to rethink their ways of working, and may even need to give up their attachment to what made them successful in the first place. There will inevitably come a point when previous success is no longer a guarantee of future success.

Madonna is a good example of relentless reinvention and innovation. She is now over 60 years old and her career has been a series of reincarnations, each one more provocative than the last. Madonna has continued to court controversy and flout tradition, attracting both positive attention and condemnation – but always staying one step ahead.

We need to change our thinking in order to change

We will often not change unless we feel the need to change. But we all have *cognitive hurdles* to overcome. These are thoughts and phrases that we resort to in order to entrench a belief or a point of view. Overcoming these cognitive hurdles requires that we look at the world around us through a different lens.

In the 1980s, the New York subway was considered one of the most dangerous places in the city. Murders on the subway were considered to be an inevitable aspect of urban life. The New York police force, most of whom did not regularly use the subway, tried to play down people's anxieties and fears.

However, this all changed in 1990 when Bill Bratton became head of the Transit Police in New York. Bratton was a supporter of the *broken window theory* posited by criminologists George Kelling and James Wilson, which says that even minor acts of vandalism will lead to more serious crime. Kelling and Wilson believed that by addressing minor offences, rates of more violent crime would be lowered.

Bratton insisted that all New York police officers, including himself, use the subway in order to experience the problems for themselves. Having observed the conditions that were creating the crimes, the police officers felt more inclined to change what was happening.

Make change easy for people

One example of making change easy for people is that some businesses are encouraging the concept of *bring your own device* (BYOD) to engage their employees on a deeper level.

If, for example, we are accustomed to using a Mac, the BYOD initiative means that we do not spend time and effort adjusting to a PC. Using devices that are available and familiar means that time can instead be focused on the application of the technology to enhance the customer experience and business productivity.

Of course there are serious concerns around security of data, loss of devices, risk of cyber attacks and greater exposure to viruses. And even though a BYOD approach may reduce hardware costs, there may be additional investment needed to support a range of different devices.

However, with technology continuing to dominate the way we work, organisations need to think more flexibly about how they keep their people engaged and productive while the technology and working landscape shifts beneath them. When people feel self-sufficient and able to work well, they are more likely to do a good job.

Mobility makes change easier

A low employee turnover is not necessarily a good thing, especially for the individuals concerned. Traditionally we have believed that moving jobs on a regular basis signified lack of commitment. Nowadays, it is becoming a more acceptable part of working life.

The longer we stay in any organisation, the more out of touch with the external world we become. Our vision narrows and we become victims of our organisation's orthodoxies or deeply ingrained beliefs. We start to believe our own propaganda and do not see any need to change.

Our brain needs new challenges and experiences to keep it active and agile. If we surround ourselves constantly with the familiar, we become stale and stagnant. Old habits dominate and suppress our desire to enquire and to learn.

Changing jobs means feeling incompetent and uncomfortable again. Most of us do not enjoy this stage in learning, but it is actually very good for us. When we feel incompetent, we strive to acquire new knowledge and skills, and the new neural connections we make keep our brain healthy and resilient. The more used we get to personal change, the better we are at dealing with organisational change.

Culture is key

Organisations may have the best strategy in the world but culture is what really counts. If a strong and positive organisational culture is not in place, strategic plans become worthless.

Successful change depends on a supportive and collaborative culture. As organisations grow, it is critical that good cultures are preserved.

The shoe company Zappos spends time carefully evaluating candidates at interview for cultural fit. New employees are offered $2,000 to leave after the first week of training if they decide that they are not in the right job. Zappos is prepared to invest in the wrong people leaving as well as in the right people staying.

The values of the company represent a fundamental part of employees' training, and a substantial portion of leaders' budgets is dedicated to team development activities. As a result Zappos' employees feel valued, motivated and productive. And Zappos' customers are happy, too.

Southwest Airlines is another organisation that spends time on ensuring good cultural fit. For 43 years it has enjoyed enormous success because of the culture it has created.

Southwest Airlines has been the subject of two PhD theses that gave rise to the book *NUTS*, which details the uniquely positive elements of the airline's culture.[10] An example is how the now-retired founder, chairman and CEO Herb Kelleher famously used to ask pilots to drop their trousers during job interviews to see if they had a sense of humour.

The organisation's underpinning philosophy is that great employees offer great service to customers.

Southwest Airlines empowers its employees to keep customers happy and it has a number of recognition awards and programmes that reinforce positive behaviour. For example, the airline's magazine *Southwest Spirit* features a story every month of an employee who has delivered exceptional customer service.

Over the years, Southwest Airlines has managed to weather increasing competition and rising fuel prices by adapting to a changing environment with a constant focus on customers and employees.

Instead of resorting to cost-cutting, the airline has looked for ways to boost revenues. For example, when other airlines imposed a baggage charge, Southwest Airlines introduced a 'Bags Fly Free' policy, which attracted new customers.

Throughout its growth, Southwest Airlines has kept a close eye on its culture and been very selective about who is brought into the fold. The airline has consistently been ranked as one of the best places to work by *Forbes*, *Fortune* and others.

Accept that expectations often drive results. Listen to the language that you use with others; this will often reveal your expectations of how the change will be. Become more aware of your own feelings, thoughts and responses to any change that you are experiencing. Remember that if you expect something to be good it is more likely to turn out that way.

Decide to change something in your life. It does not have to be a big change: any change is good. Try eating something different, take a new route to work, talk to someone you do not know very well. Above all, break simple routines on a regular basis. If we make regular changes in our life we stay agile, flexible, open-minded and robust.

Acquire good habits that keep you healthy and strong. These include sleep and exercise. Personal resilience is essential when life becomes more unpredictable and uncertain. Make sure that the people in your life support decisions that you make involving change. A caring and encouraging social network is essential to our happiness and wellbeing.

Picture a future state that takes you away from your present and comfort zone. Find something about the future that could be rewarding in order to motivate you to keep moving forward, even when you feel tempted to revert to what you already know. Lasting change depends on persistence and tenacity.

Transform your negative thoughts and words. Use the language of hope and aspiration when you talk about your own plans and ambitions. Challenge your own cognitive hurdles and try to see the world through a different lens.

References for Chapter 9

1 Eisenberger, N. (2012) 'The neural bases of social pain: evidence for shared representations with physical pain', *Psychosomatic Medicine*, February, 126–35

2 Robison, J. (2012) 'Wellbeing is contagious (for better or worse): how one employee's wellbeing affects that of the entire team', *Gallup Business Journal*, 27 November [gallup.com]

3 Haeffel, G.J. & J.L. Hames (2013) 'Cognitive vulnerability to depression can be contagious', *Clinical Psychological Science*, April, 75–85

4 Coghill, R.C. et al. (2003) 'Neural correlates of interindividual differences in the subjective experience of pain', *Proceedings for the National Academy of Sciences*, July, 8538–42

5 Wise, E. et al. (2002) 'Gender role expectations of pain: relationship to experimental pain perception', *Pain*, April 335–42

6 Glasser, W. (1998) *Choice Theory: A New Psychology of Personal Freedom*. New York: HarperCollins

7 Uhls, Y.T. et al. (2014) 'Five days at outdoor education camp without screens improves preteen skills with nonverbal emotion cues', *Computers in Human Behaviour*, October, 387–92

8 Rhudy, J.L. & M.W. Meaghe (2000) 'Fear and anxiety: divergent effects on human pain thresholds', *Pain*, January, 65–75

9 Cialdini, R. (2007) *Influence: The Psychology of Persuasion*. New York: Collins

10 Frieberg, K. & J. Frieberg (1998) *NUTS! Southwest Airlines' Crazy Recipe for Business and Personal Success*. New York: Broadway Books

'When stress is the basic state of mind, even good things stress us out. We have to learn to let go.'

Sakyong Mipham

Head of the Shambhala Buddhist lineage and Shambhala International (1962–)

10: OUR BRAIN AND STRESS

About this chapter

Stress is a highly subjective phenomenon and is different for everyone. We do not all find the same things stressful, and there is considerable variation in the way we each respond to stress.

With the pressures of today's world, stress is pervasive and the term *stress* is frequently used to describe numerous conditions. Many of us are so used to feeling stressed that it has become a norm that we no longer question.

There are different symptoms of stress, including cognitive, behavioural, physiological and physical indicators.

This chapter discusses the signs and impact of stress on our brain and body, and offers tips to enable us to deal with stressors in our world.

Part 1: The science explained

What is stress?

Stress is a biological and psychological response that we experience when we encounter a threat that we feel we do not have the resources to deal with.

Stress was first referred to in 1936 by Hans Selye,[1] a Hungarian endocrinologist, who defined it as:

'the non-specific response of the body to any demand for change'

Selye explained that any threat or *stressor* that is challenging, threatening or demanding (e.g. giving a presentation, taking an exam, divorce, death, moving house, loss of job) can result in a three-stage response:

1 Alarm
When we encounter a stressor, our body reacts with the *fight or flight* response and our *sympathetic nervous system* is activated. Hormones, such as *cortisol* and *adrenaline*, are released into the bloodstream to give our body additional strength and energy to meet the stressor.

2 Resistance
Our body focuses resources against the stressor. Our blood glucose levels remain high, and cortisol and adrenaline continue to circulate at elevated levels. Our body remains in a state of high alertness, with heart rate and breathing accelerated.

3 Exhaustion
If the stressor continues beyond our body's capacity to respond or cope, we exhaust our resources and run out of defences, becoming susceptible to disease and death.

How do we get stressed?

Our brain and body assess whether or not a situation is stressful. This decision is made based on how we receive and process new sensory inputs and how our stored memories inform us about the last time we were in a similar situation.

Overall, we need to maintain a regular balance, or homeostasis.

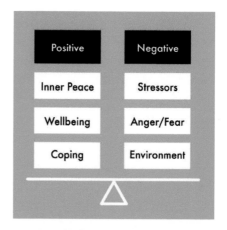

When we do not have homeostasis, such as when we are out of balance, we feel the effects of stress.

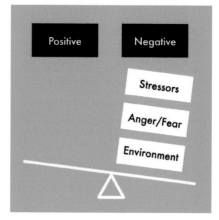

Our master gland

In our brain, the *hypothalamus* and the *pituitary gland* together constitute our master gland in charge of our body's stress response. They work by activating our *adrenal glands*, which are situated next to our kidneys:

» The **adrenal medulla** on the inner part of the adrenal gland produces hormones such as *adrenaline*, which helps our body respond quickly to a threat in our environment.

» The **adrenal cortex** on the outer part of the adrenal gland produces hormones such as *cortisol*, which helps regulate our metabolism, and *aldosterone*, which helps to control blood pressure.

The more stress we have, the more our brain resorts to *fight or flight* mode, which in turn activates two endocrine systems that secrete chemicals, such as hormones, to help us deal with the stressor (see Figure 10.1).

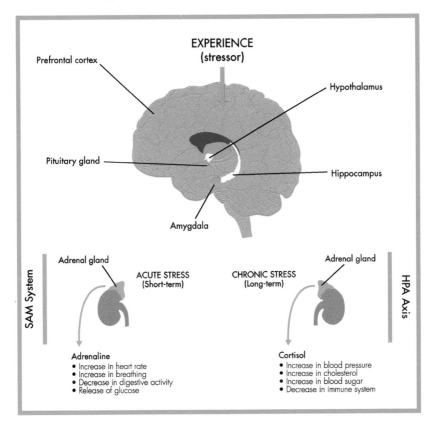

Figure 10.1: Our two stress pathways

These two systems are:

1) Sympathetic-adrenal-medullary (SAM) system

When the *SAM system* is fired, the adrenal medulla secretes the hormone adrenaline, which creates the following changes in the body:

» Increase in heart rate
» Increase in breathing
» Decrease in digestive activity
» Release of glucose for energy

As soon as the perceived threat has passed, the parasympathetic nervous system takes control and restores balance in the body. The sympathetic and parasympathetic systems are designed to work together in balance: when one part is working, the other stops, as discussed in more detail in Chapter 1, Our Brain. This is detailed in Figure 10.2.

In relatively small amounts, stress can sharpen our concentration and help us to stay focused, energetic and alert. Stress can even give us extra strength to defend ourselves and overcome challenges.

However, a build-up of stress can cause major damage to our brain and body.

2) Hypothalamic-pituitary-adrenal (HPA) axis

Longer-term stress is regulated by the HPA axis. The hypothalamus stimulates the pituitary gland to activate the adrenal cortex, which releases cortisol. Cortisol enables the body to maintain steady supplies of blood sugar so we can cope with the stressor on a prolonged basis. Cortisol also releases stored glucose from the liver (for energy) and helps control swelling after injury. The immune system is suppressed while this happens.

Over time, stress can directly and indirectly contribute to general or specific physiological and psychological disorders. Long-term stress raises adrenaline and cortisol levels in our body, which in turn increases heart rate, respiration and blood pressure, and places more physical stress on bodily organs.

Elevated cortisol levels are especially harmful since cortisol suppresses the immune system by metabolising white blood cells. As the number of white blood cells lowers, the efficiency of the immune system decreases, leaving the body open to infection and disease. Blood pressure is also raised, resulting in hypertension and atherosclerosis, both precursors to cardiovascular disease.

Body	Parasympathetic 'Rest and Digest'	Sympathetic 'Fight or Flight'
Eyes	Pupils constrict	Pupils dilate
Salivary glands	Saliva production increases	Saliva production reduces
Nose	Mucus production increases	Mucus production reduces
Heart	Heart rate slows	Heart rate increases
Lung	Bronchial muscles contract	Bronchial muscles relax
Stomach	Gastric juices and digestion increase	Digestion reduces
Liver	Normal function	Glucose increases
Kidneys	Urine increases	Urine decreases
Adrenal glands	Normal function	Adrenaline is released

Figure 10.2: The parasympathetic and sympathetic nervous systems

And so, if our stress hormones are not metabolised, their cumulative build-up can be a contributing factor in heart disease, high blood pressure, stroke and other illnesses.

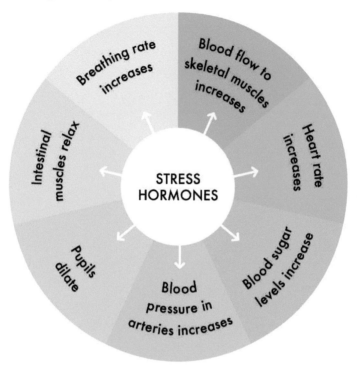

Figure 10.3: The effects of stress hormones on our body

Causes of stress

There are a number of factors that cause stress:

External

» Biological and ecological factors (diet, pollution, working conditions)
» Major life changes
» Work or school
» Relationship difficulties

» Financial problems
» Being too busy
» Technostress (information overload, loss of privacy, reduced boundaries, digital divide)
» Children and family
» Occupational stress (uncertainty, demands, travel)
» Other (health, academic)

Internal

» Chronic worry
» Pessimism
» Rigid thinking, lack of flexibility
» Negative self-talk
» Unrealistic expectations/perfectionism
» All-or-nothing attitude

Stress can shrink our brain

Research is increasingly highlighting the effect that stress has on the physical structure of our brain.

When we are stressed over a period of time, our brain adapts to the higher levels of cortisol present in our body and our hippocampus starts to shrink. This is why when we have been stressed for a while we become more forgetful.

Because we do not all respond to stress in the same way, we may experience different symptoms of stress. However, there are several common warning signs of stress, as highlighted in Figure 10.4, overleaf.

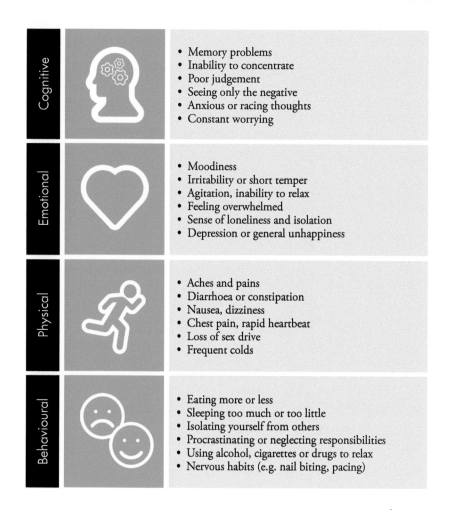

Figure 10.4: Warning signs of stress

The hippocampus is also one of the first areas of the brain to be affected by dementia. The fact that stressors over our lifetime could trigger the development of dementia is a key area of research today. A study has even revealed that people who have experienced significant stress are 65% more likely to develop dementia.[2]

Yale researchers looked at healthy participants who had experienced a stressful event such as the death of a loved one, loss of a home, loss of a job or divorce.[3]

Even those participants who had only recently experienced a stressful event showed reduced volume in the prefrontal cortex, the region of the brain that regulates emotions and self-control.

How do we measure stress?

There are many different ways of measuring stress. A variety of questionnaires assess the psychological and physiological factors associated with stress:

» The **psychological factors** include feelings of wellbeing, self-efficacy (belief in our ability to exert control over our life) and cognitive ability.

» The **physiological factors** include activation of the sympathetic nervous system, sleep, gastrointestinal, upper-respiratory and cardiopulmonary symptoms.

An objective measure of stress is to measure the stress hormones (cortisol and adrenaline) in blood, saliva, urine or hair. Cortisol is often used as a biological measure of chronic stress and is easily measured in saliva and, more recently, hair samples. Cortisol tends to fluctuate during the day and is higher in the morning, which is why hair samples tend to offer a more stable reading than urine or saliva.

Part 2: Impact on our daily life

What we think is stressful will be stressful

Our brain cannot always differentiate between the imagined and the real. It is enough for us to think that something is stressful for it to become stressful. Stress is therefore a subjective phenomenon. Whether the threat is real or not is irrelevant; the brain will respond in the same way to a difficult meeting with the boss as it would to a meeting with a wild animal!

We prepare ourselves for physical survival on a regular basis, even though our life is not actually under threat. We cannot eliminate the threat and fight (punch the boss) or flee (run out of a meeting room), and so we become more aggressive, impatient, anxious and hyper-reactive.

Can stress be good for us?

The *Yerkes–Dodson law* was developed in 1908 by the psychologists Robert Yerkes and John Dillingham Dodson.

Yerkes and Dodson used mild electrical shocks to motivate rats to run around a maze in the correct order. However, as the shocks intensified, the rats tried to escape by running in random directions.

While the mild shocks were motivational the intense shocks had the opposite effect.

The Yerkes–Dodson law suggests that there is a relationship between performance and stress. It states that a certain level of stress can help improve performance, but beyond a specific point, performance becomes impaired (shown in Figure 10.5).

So stress enables most of us to sharpen our focus in the short term: we can study for exams, compete in a sporting event or deliver a presentation. But too much stress can overwhelm us and lead to breakdown or burnout.

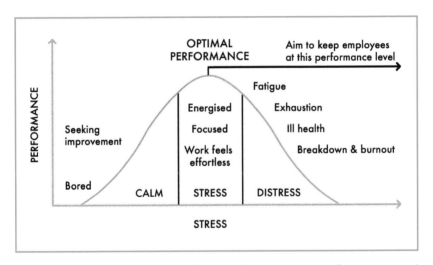

Figure 10.5: The Yerkes–Dodson Human Performance and Stress Curve

The dividing line between enough and too much stress is different for each of us and will also depend on the complexity of the task. For simpler tasks we may be able to cope with more pressure, while for more complex tasks that require more of our cognitive resources, we may find that our threshold is lower.

Our braking system

When we feel stressed and emotional, we lose our ability to think rationally: resources are diverted away from our frontal lobe and we focus instead on defensive coping strategies.

But our brain has a *braking system*, which is situated in the right prefrontal cortex.[4] The significance of this brain region is also discussed in Chapter 11, Our Brain and Leadership, as it is where we regulate our emotions.

Although this braking system has a limited capacity, it can be strengthened over time as we become more accustomed to dealing with emotional events. When we switch on our braking system, our emotional responses lose their intensity.

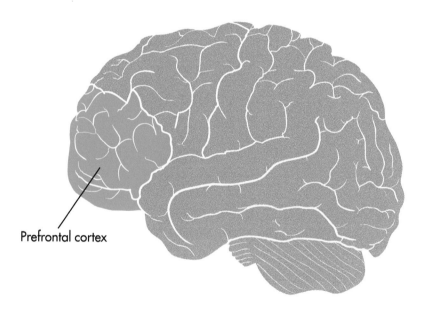

Prefrontal cortex

Figure 10.6: Our braking system

So how do we apply the brakes?

» **Label**
The first step is to label the emotion. When we articulate and try to understand our emotions, we are applying rational thought and this activates our prefontal cortex. When we suppress emotions, they tend to build up in our brain, taking on greater significance and often affecting later judgement and decision-making.

» **Reframe**
The second step is to reframe what the stressful event means to us.

An experiment was conducted where participants were shown a picture of people crying outside a church and were told that it was a picture of a funeral.

The participants were then asked to look at the same picture as a wedding ceremony.

When the participants reframed the scene as a wedding, their brain activity changed. Their brains' emotional responses reduced and their prefrontal lobe function became more active.

The power of meditation and mindfulness

In recent years, *meditation* and *mindfulness* have been discussed and debated as interlinked and overlapping concepts. So what are the main differences between them and what do they do?

Both meditation and mindfulness are ancient practices originating in religion. Meditation encompasses a number of techniques aimed at regulating consciousness and concentration in order to transcend and manage emotions. Mindfulness is one of the techniques used in meditation and involves focusing completely on the present in order to reduce the intrusion of various emotions.

The underpinning philosophy of mindfulness is that a better awareness of the present leads to greater appreciation of our surroundings. We are also more equipped to notice signs of stress or anxiety earlier and therefore deal with them more quickly.

Various studies have highlighted the health benefits of meditation and mindfulness and, in particular, their usefulness in reducing stress-related conditions such as depression, anxiety, chronic pain, diabetes and high blood pressure.

A recent study investigated the impact of mindfulness on patients who were suffering from *generalised anxiety disorder* (GAD).[5]

After eight weeks of practising mindfulness there was a significant reduction in patients' anxiety levels.

During mindfulness, our brainwaves slow down and move from a beta to an alpha rhythm. We move into alpha rhythms before sleep, as explained in Chapter 12, Our Brain and Lifestyle. Alpha rhythms have also been linked with creativity, as mentioned in Chapter 8, Our Brain and Creativity.

Alpha waves reduce the impact of distracting sensory information and help the brain to focus.[6] Brain-imaging studies even show that regular mindfulness meditation results in structural changes to the brain and increases the connections and blood flow between brain cells, leading to reduced depression and insomnia and increased compassion.[7]

A recent meta-analysis of 20 studies has highlighted how mindfulness meditation results in changes in two brain areas.[8] The first area, the *anterior cingulate cortex* (ACC), which is associated with emotional regulation, problem-solving and decision-making and which is particularly important to us during periods of fast change, shows more activity after mindfulness meditation. The second area, the *hippocampus*, which is associated with memory and emotion and is susceptible to damage by chronic stress, shows greater volume of grey matter.

Mindfulness meditation is therefore instrumental in increasing our brain's overall performance and size.

Magnetic resourcing imaging (MRI) studies show how mindfulness causes the amygdala, the region of the brain involved in the body's stress response, to shrink.[9]

The connections between the amygdala and other brain regions weaken, while the prefrontal cortex, which enables us to focus and pay attention, grows thicker.

And so as we practise exercising our thoughts and rotating our attention to the present, our primal responses become less relevant and influential.

However, it is also important to point out that mindfulness should not be viewed as a tool to help employers increase the productivity of their workforce, or an excuse to abdicate responsibility for fostering a healthy working environment. To do that would defeat its purpose as a means of disconnecting momentarily from the world in order to reflect and slow down.

Moreover, mindfulness is not a cure-all for stress and health issues. It has even been criticised for triggering traumatic memories, particularly among the hypersensitive or those suffering from post-traumatic stress disorder, where painful memories may resurface. Understanding that mindfulness is a therapeutic intervention that needs initial research is therefore an important first step towards engaging in any relevant techniques.

It is also useful to balance any stress management practice with other methods of relaxation, such as reading, spending time with friends and simply taking a break. While this may seem like common sense, it is often the last thing we feel like doing when we are feeling overwhelmed or at a low ebb.

Part 3: Stories and top tips

Are our jobs killing us?

In 1983 *Time* magazine's June cover story referred to stress as 'The Epidemic of the Eighties'.

Since then stress has become an ever-more pervasive term, with job stress being the number one source of stress for adults. The Japanese trend of *karoshi*, or *death from overwork*, is believed to be due to heart attack and stroke caused by high levels of stress. It is now estimated that the majority of all visits to doctors are for stress-related problems.

Experts state that it is not easy to predict who will suffer from stress as a result of work-related pressures. Other factors should also be taken into consideration, such as social network, family life and genetic predisposition. However, there has recently been an increase in reports about stress and its impact on psychological and physical health.

The United Kingdom Health and Safety Executive (HSE) estimates the costs to society of work-related stress to be approximately £4 billion each year, while in 2010 the European Commission reported that among professionals with work-related ill health, 'stress, depression or anxiety' was a serious health problem. The European Survey of Enterprises on New and Emerging Risks (ESENER, 2010) has also found that 79% of European managers are concerned about stress in their workplaces. It is clear that the impact of stress is far-reaching, and has often been exacerbated by recent economic difficulties.

With the financial crisis of 2008, reported incidents of mental illness and stress increased in line with people's worries about money and job insecurity. Executives now report feeling unable to cope or make simple decisions. Perhaps more worryingly, studies have shown that over time chronic long-term stress destroys brain cells and damages the hippocampus, the region of the brain involved in the formation and retrieval of memories. This may explain why the more pressure people feel they are under, the more forgetful they become.

Stress can affect anyone

Today's working environment is punishing for many working executives. But admitting to being stressed has always carried a stigma, particularly in male-dominated, competitive environments where stress is sometimes associated with weakness or incompetence.

However, recent reports of senior executives having to take time off work to recover from stress-related illness have made the business world sit up and take note. Stress is no longer an affliction that hits the lower levels of the hierarchy, involved in repetitive and routine tasks; even those at the top are not immune from suffering from exhaustion and burnout.

And a healthy pay packet, it seems, does not offer any protection against this.

A medical experiment was undertaken with well-paid football managers.

These managers were wired up to a monitor that gauged their blood pressure and heart rate during crucial games such as those that determined which team was to be promoted or relegated.

The results were dramatic, with managers' heart rates reaching potentially dangerous levels, making them vulnerable to cardiac arrest or severe angina.

We can all do something to help others

Yukio Shige is a 70-year-old retired police officer who patrols the Tojinbo cliffs in Fukui Prefecture, Japan, a popular tourist destination and a well-known spot for people to commit suicide. Over the last decade Mr Shige has prevented an estimated 500 suicides. After a friend tragically committed suicide, Mr Shige decided that he wanted to help others. Now known as the *Chotto matte* ('Hold on, wait') man, he goes to the cliffs every day, carrying binoculars and accompanied by his three volunteers.

Japan has one of the highest suicide rates in the world, with an estimated 30,000 people killing themselves every year. During the 1998 financial crisis the number went up by a third. The numbers rose again after the 2008 worldwide financial crisis. Around 40% of young people in Japan are unable to find stable jobs and the fastest-growing suicide demographic is young men. Suicide is now the single biggest killer of men in Japan aged between 20 and 44.

Japanese culture discourages complaining or the expression of strong emotions from an early age. In particular, feelings that may be associated with weakness, such as anxiety or stress, are often suppressed. Different methods of stress relief have emerged over the years to enable people to release and share their emotions at work, such as the recent practice of hiring *ikemesos*, men who come into offices and show women emotive videos and pictures to encourage them to cry.[10]

For men it is more difficult. Cultural pressures, combined with high youth unemployment and technology-based communication, have led to the social phenomenon of *hikikomori*, ('confined' or 'pulled inward') – young, mainly male, Japanese who withdraw from society. Similar cases have recently been reported in Western countries, too.[11]

Mr Shige and his team do not just bring people back from the cliff edge; they also help people get their lives back. He has been reported as saying:

'If they're in debt, I take them to legal aid people; if they're out of work, I take them to the Hello Work employment agency; if they're homeless, I take them home with me.'

Exercise reduces stress

Exercise reduces the effects of stress by lowering levels of the body's stress hormones, such as adrenaline and cortisol. Exercise also stimulates the production of endorphins, our natural painkillers.

Raising our heart rate can actually reverse damage to the brain caused by stressful events and can stimulate growth in the hippocampal region, which shrinks when we are stressed.

When we exercise we also produce noradrenaline/norepinephrine, which is associated with improved cognitive function and learning.

The effects of exercise are immediate. Just after exercise our mood is better and our energy is higher. And even though exercise produces cortisol, our level returns to normal very quickly afterwards.

According to Dr Robert Leahy, Director of the American Institute for Cognitive Therapy and author of *Beat the Blues Before They Beat You*:

'Exercise is like free medicine. Medication may work more rapidly to lessen the symptoms of depression or stressed feelings, but the effects of regular exercise are longer lasting.'

Set realistic goals and be patient with yourself. Pause regularly throughout the day: take a break from sitting at a desk every 20 to 30 minutes. Learn to prioritise what is really important. When we try to take on too much, we cause problems for ourselves and add to our stress levels.

Master your emotions and learn how to express and articulate how you feel. This will enable you to deal with your emotions more effectively. Know your own personal stress triggers and tolerance to stress, particularly when dealing with personal adversity. Seek to address these before they turn into bigger problems.

Introduce moments of calm and serenity into your day. Let your mind rest. Disconnect mentally from all the noise around you. Use mindfulness techniques to focus on the present and reduce the impact of anxious thoughts. Breathe slowly – this will help you think more calmly and clearly.

Laugh with your social network of friends and family; share happy experiences and build positive memories together. Loneliness makes us more vulnerable to stress. An environment where we feel supported, nurtured and loved is essential to our mental wellbeing and ability to cope with life's pressures.

Elevate your mood with exercise. Carve out some personal time to focus on your health and wellbeing. Devote time and effort to building a strong, capable and resilient system that will enable you to manage life's challenges.

References for Chapter 10

1 Seyle, H. (1978) *The Stress of Life*. New York: McGraw-Hill
2 Johansson, L. et al. (2010) 'Midlife psychological stress and risk of dementia: a 35-year longitudinal population study', *Brain*, August, 2217–24
3 Ansell, E.B. et al. (2012) 'Cumulative adversity and smaller gray matter volume in medial prefrontal, anterior cingulate, and insula regions', *Biological Psychiatry*, July, 57–64
4 Lieberman, M.D. (2009). 'The brain's braking system (and how to "use your words" to tap into it)', *NeuroLeadership*, September, 9–14
5 Majid, S.A. (2012) 'Effect of mindfulness based stress management on reduction of generalized anxiety disorder', *Iranian Journal of Public Health*, October, 24–28
6 Sacchet, M.D. et al. (2015) 'Attention drives synchronization of alpha and beta rhythms between right inferior frontal and primary sensory neocortex', *Journal of Neuroscience*, February, 2074–82
7 Hölzel B. et al. (2011) 'Mindfulness practice leads to increases in regional brain gray matter density', *Psychiatry Research*, January, 36–43
8 Congelton, C. et al. (2015) 'Mindfulness can literally change your brain', *Harvard Business Review*, January, 309–18
9 Taren, A.A. et al. (2013) 'Dispositional mindfulness co-varies with smaller amygdala and caudate volumes in community adults', *PLOS ONE*, May [doi.org/10.1371/journal.pone.0064574]
10 Paul, C. (2016) 'Behind the strange Japanese trend to cope with stress', *Time*, 10 August [time.com]
11 Kato, T.A. et al. (2012) 'Does the "hikikomori" syndrome of social withdrawal exist outside Japan? A preliminary international investigation', *Social Psychiatry and Psychiatric Epidemiology*, July, 1061–75

'The future depends on
what we do in the present.'

Mahatma Gandhi

Lawyer, politician, social activist and writer
(1869–1948)

11: OUR BRAIN AND LEADERSHIP

About this chapter

O ur appetite for learning about leadership shows no sign of abating. From the latest theories presented by business schools, to biographies of high achievers and self-help guides with easy-to-follow steps, we continue to reach for new tools and practical solutions based on others' tried and tested successes.

But can we really distil leadership into several key nuggets that can be replicated across a wider population? Consistent and effective leadership still seems to be an elusive concept that is hard to define and pin down.

This chapter discusses how our brain works within the context of the leadership role and why leaders could benefit from an understanding of the workings of the human brain.

Part 1: The science explained

What can neuroscience teach us about leadership?

All leaders affect the brainpower of the people they lead. It is therefore essential that leaders understand how the human brain works.

But finding good leaders appears to be a worldwide problem. A recent Global Workforce Leadership Survey found that as baby boomers (born between 1946 and 1964) retire, leadership will be the hardest skill to find in the remaining workforce.[1] A report entitled *Business Human Capital Challenges Today and in the Future*, from the Society of

Figure 11.1: Leaders affect the brains of those they lead

Human Resource Management (SHRM), also found that the availability of the next generation of leaders is a pressing concern for businesses today.[2]

Neuroscientists are now affording us a glimpse into how particular brain-coordinated activity, or *coherence*, may manifest itself in good leadership practices.[3] The higher the coherence, the better the brain is at executing complex tasks that require a high level of communication between its regions.

If we look at the leadership role as comprising several key activities, such as decision-making, communication and emotional self-regulation, these activities all require the multiple skills that constitute our executive functioning. And the seat of our executive functioning is the *frontal lobe*.

In one study, the brain activity of leaders was monitored using electrodes while they were asked a few questions about their goals for their companies.

Those leaders who were deemed by their employees to be inspirational were found to generate higher levels of activity in the *right frontal lobe*, an area responsible for interpersonal communication and social relationships.[4]

Right frontal lobe activity is now considered to be essential for inspirational leadership.

It is important to add that antisocial behaviours and poor social skills often arise from damage to the right frontal lobe.[5]

The frontal lobe helps us not only to make decisions but also to make the right decisions. In the wake of recent corporate scandals, ethical decision-making has received a great deal of attention. Some organisations have made a point of communicating their own moral compass to the world – consider Google's catchphrase 'Don't be evil'.

The way the frontal and temporal lobes communicate with each other is particularly significant to leadership as this communication involves the interpretation and management of emotional signals. Our brain's ability to assess and use emotions appropriately is what is now referred to as *emotional intelligence*, a term that has been popularised by Daniel Goleman.[6]

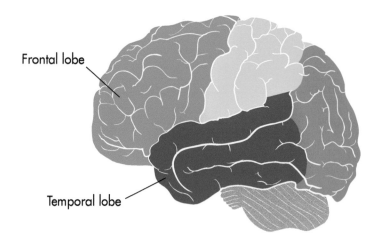

Figure 11.2: The frontal and temporal lobes

Are there chemicals of leadership?

Leaders need to manage the balance of chemicals that drive their behaviour and emotion.

Individuals high in *testosterone*, for example, are more likely to be seen as dominant and confident, and issues arise when leaders are overly competitive. High levels of testosterone and *dopamine* in overly competitive leaders reduce *oxytocin* levels and hence the ability to be empathetic with others. This finding applies just as much to women as to men.

Equal balance needs to be found between *serotonin* (maintaining an upbeat mood), *oxytocin* (building trust), *dopamine* (motivation) and *noradrenaline* (alertness and focus).

| Serotonin | Oxytocin | Dopamine | Noradrenaline |

Leaders can also promote chemical release in the people working around them, by reinforcing and rewarding certain behaviours.

When we are given the freedom to find solutions for ourselves, our brain rewards itself with neurotransmitters such as dopamine and noradrenaline. When we build positive relationships and forge bonds of trust, we release serotonin and oxytocin.

Why do traditional leadership practices not work?

Douglas McGregor's two theories of motivation – *Theory X* and *Theory Y* – were first published back in the 1960s.[7]

Theory X Assumes that people must be controlled, directed and motivated by the threat of punishment.

Theory Y Proposes that people will direct their own effort, seek responsibility and be committed to their organisation when they are valued and respected.

In most leadership practices today, Theory X is still very much in evidence: we continue to assume that effort has to be directed through incentives and that mistakes often result in punitive measures.

The problem with systems that focus on reward or punishment is that people's attention is directed to precisely that, and not on generating new and creative ways to solve problems. As explained in Chapter 4, Our Brain and Attention, the attentional system is limited and if it is aimed in one direction, by default it is aimed away from another. So if people are concerned with avoiding pitfalls and failure, their brain will not be able to entertain innovative approaches or solutions.

Even when leaders believe that they are adopting a more people-centred and empathetic approach by devoting time to listening and consultation, the carrot-and-stick approach is often used in the end. As discussed in Chapter 5, Our Brain and Language, the traditional performance appraisal is a case in point: it may be communicated as an opportunity to review progress and plan development, but in reality it is often viewed as a means of evaluating a shortfall of effort against objectives.

No matter how much the performance appraisal is dressed up to look positive, a negative message is frequently all that is registered. For example, even the use of words such as 'constructive' or 'developmental' carries a subtext that feels like fault-finding to the person on the receiving end.

Typical questions that are frequently used in business to direct people to the right answer include 'What effect do you think that had on the team?' and 'How do you think you should have done it?'

These are seemingly positive. But these questions fail to take into account the brain's negativity bias or the fact that people's previous experiences have often conditioned them to anticipate impending disapproval. Either way, the brain responds to these as an attack and immediately builds its necessary defences.

The still-pervasive influence of Theory X in leadership practices across many organisations means that leaders, however well intentioned, may never really get the best out of their people.

Leaders can help us reshape our brain

When we focus our attention on anything over time, we create changes in the brain's structure, as explained in Chapter 4, Our Brain and Attention. Attention needs to be directed and purposeful focus will prevent people from dwelling on what is unhelpful.

Environment is critical. If we are given the space to concentrate and pay attention then our brain will create the right internal conditions to think, develop insights and make improvements. Our neural networks adapt to the work we do and the way we do it – and over time we physically change our brain. This is known as *self-directed neuroplasticity*.

Leaders therefore have a significant role to play in the brain development of their people. The right or the wrong environment can have a neurological impact that should not be underestimated.

Expectations drive results

Leaders' expectations of their people are often the catalyst that can bring about good or bad performance in those same people. Leaders can either choose to see the spark in someone or they can choose not to. The same person who has been a failure under one leader can shine under another. It is often the expectation of the leader that drives results.

This is what we call the *Pygmalion* or *Expectation effect*. In Greek mythology, Pygmalion was a sculptor who fell in love with his own carving of a statue. Leaders' beliefs about their people quickly become reality.

In 1963, two researchers, Rosenthal and Jacobson, tested children at an elementary (primary) school in California with an IQ test called the Test of General Ability at the beginning of the school year.[8] The teachers were told that the test was a measure of academic 'blooming'.

In reality, the test had no such predictive validity. At the school, 18 teachers were informed of the students in their classes who had obtained scores in the top percentile. However, these students had actually been chosen by the researchers at random.

The teachers were told that at the end of the school year the same test would be used again to determine any differences in IQ.

The results were astounding. There was a marked difference in IQ test scores between the students labelled as 'blooming' and those who had not been labelled in this way. These results were strongest in the youngest children (aged between five and seven years old).

Rosenthal and Jacobson's results clearly demonstrate the power of expectation over results. This is what we call a *self-fulfilling prophecy*.

It was the expectations of the teachers that led to the pupils' increased (or decreased) performance, with the younger children being more susceptible to teaching influences than older children.

Self-awareness is the hallmark of effective leadership

Much has been made about the importance of self-awareness in leadership. Self-awareness demands an ability to be open to feedback from others and sometimes to hear messages that are unexpected or even unwelcome. We do not always see ourselves the way other people see us, as the Scottish poet Robert Burns said:

**'O wad some Pow'r the giftie gie us
To see oursels as ithers see us!
It wad frae mony a blunder free us.'**

The English translation is:

**'And would some Power give
us the gift
To see ourselves as others see us!
It would from many a blunder free us.'**

Tools such as the *JoHari Window* are designed to encourage disclosure that people feel comfortable with.

Created by Joseph Luft and Harry Ingham in 1955, the JoHari Window is a tool that enables us to learn about aspects of ourselves that we may otherwise not have been aware of.

The tool is based on a four-quadrant model (see Figure 11.3):

» **The open area** represents what we know about ourselves and are willing to share. The more we feel able to disclose about ourselves and can learn from others, the higher the level of trust we can build between us.

» **The blind area** represents what we do not know about ourselves but others can see. If we are able to accept

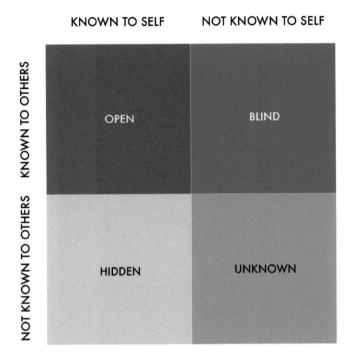

Figure 11.3: The JoHari Window

feedback from others, we can become aware of these characteristics or behaviours.

» **The hidden area** represents what we are aware of but may not want others to know.

» **The unknown area** represents what is not known to either us or anyone else.

With different people, we choose different degrees of disclosure. The more we learn from other people about our own behaviour and impact, the more we increase our open area and reduce the blind area. And through self-discovery and collaboration with others, we are better able to build constructive networks that contribute to our continuing growth and development.

Coaching is an effective way of maintaining self-awareness and enhancing personal insight. If coaching is linked to and supports a development programme, it increases the chances of the new learning becoming embedded in new habits and skills.

In 1997 a study of managers found that a training programme alone increased productivity by 28%.

When coaching was provided to support the training, productivity increased by 88%.[9]

Leadership and trust

Our brains are equipped with social antennae for determining how trustworthy others are. We rapidly determine whether someone is or is not trustworthy through the activation of our *mirror neurons*, or *circuits of empathy* – as discussed in Chapter 2, Our Brain and Emotion.

Our mirror neurons reflect the behaviour that someone else is exhibiting and then prompt a response in return. If we are angry, negative or nervous this is recognised by others very quickly.

Our brain is designed to build trust gradually and when we start building a bond with someone we release oxytocin, which makes us trust that person even more.

We make a judgement within seconds whether we trust other people and we are heavily influenced by facial expression and face shape. Recent research has demonstrated that a face that looks happy, with upturned eyebrows and an upward curve to the mouth, is likely to be seen as trustworthy (see Figure 11.4). A face that looks angry, with downturned eyebrows, is viewed as untrustworthy.[10]

Figure 11.4: The face, trust and competence

Credit: Professor John Freeman, New York University

Because trustworthiness can be inferred from facial expressions, it can sometimes be faked, which is why we may occasionally find ourselves trusting the wrong person.

We assess competence slightly differently – on the basis of facial width. The wider the face, the more competence is perceived. A wider face has been linked to higher levels of testosterone and hence greater strength and aggression, which may have an evolutionary foundation: strength means a greater chance of survival.

The smile

Research into the smile has an interesting history. For four decades researchers have been associating the human smile with the chimpanzee *fear smile*, which is a submissive gesture and used to defuse any potential aggression. When a chimp uses this fear smile, they are indicating that they are safe and do not pose a threat. Our human smile also has a submissive element because we often use it to defuse any potential hostility or when we are feeling nervous.

However, new evidence also suggests that our smile may also be linked to a joyful state of mind.[11] When comparing the chimpanzee smile used in play to the human smile, a number of similarities have been observed. While chimpanzees continue to use this smile in play conditions, the human smile has evolved into a more sophisticated communication tool.

The importance of the smile in the business context must not be underestimated. The affirmative connotations of the smile mean that if leaders smile more they are more likely to stimulate positive facial expressions and hence positive feelings in the people around them.

And, as mentioned above, an upturned mouth is associated with a trustworthy character.

Part 2: Impact on our daily life

The environment that leaders create is critical

Leaders are responsible for the environments they create around them and the communities that they encourage people to join. We all work best when we are part of a caring and inclusive network.

Our ability to interact with others has given us an evolutionary advantage over other animals, with the result that our brains have grown larger as we have developed social networks and learned to cooperate more with each other.[12]

But tough and competitive working environments, where there is a high risk of rejection, can be painful for us on a neurological as well as an emotional level. Our brain's pain receptors fire equally when stimulated by either social pain or physical pain.[13] And the effects of social pain often remain for much longer than the effects of purely physical pain.

■ social pain
■ physical pain

Figure 11.5: Social and physical pain in the brain

Status		Our sense of status is one of the most significant predictors of long-term health. Research has shown that, in monkeys, status is equal to survival.[14] When we perceive a threat to our status, we will respond defensively, as if we are facing a real threat. When we feel that we are learning, and when we are given positive feedback, our status goes up.
Certainty		Because our brain is a prediction machine it craves certainty. Even a small amount of uncertainty can create the sensation in the *orbital frontal cortex* and the *anterior cingulate cortex* that 'something is wrong'. Certainty feels good because it is predictable. Being kept continually involved and informed with clear messages, particularly during times of change, increases our feelings of certainty.
Autonomy		When we feel that we have control over our work, we reduce our stress levels. Micromanagement, which reduces our feelings of control, feels threatening to us and can provoke a stress response in us. Feeling able to control our own workflow, manage our time at work and make decisions all contribute to a greater sense of autonomy.
Relatedness		We need to feel that we belong to a social group. We feel comfortable with people who are like us. Our brain searches for similarities because similarities make us feel safe. When we trust people, we collaborate with them. When we collaborate with other people, we share information. Small groups feel less intimidating than big groups because a small group offers more opportunities to connect with others.
Fairness		When we experience feelings of unfairness or injustice our *insula* activates. This is the region of the brain that is triggered when we experience disgust or revulsion, as well as when punishment is dispensed for selfishness or greed. The insula is the part of the brain linked to social and moral behaviour. Both transparency of decision-making and equal treatment of others ensure that fairness is maintained.

Figure 11.6: Dr David Rock's SCARF model

According to the neuroscientist Dr David Rock,[15] there are five key considerations that leaders should understand since they affect how we operate at work and with other people (see Figure 11.6).

Temperature and noise affect our productivity

Our environment – temperature, colour and noise – affects our productivity.[16] Studies have shown that natural daylight makes us more alert and less stressed than artificial lighting.[17]

Different office temperatures have also been tested by Cornell University, with results showing that working at low room temperatures (20°C or 68°F) lead to 44% more mistakes than working at optimal room temperature (25°C or 77°F). Because our energy is being diverted to keeping warm, we are less likely to focus and pay attention to our work. Warm environments also make us happier.

Participants were divided into two groups: one group was asked to test heating pads and the other group was asked to test ice packs.[18]

They were asked questions about either their actual employer or a hypothetical company.

Those whose hands were warm (heating pads) expressed higher job satisfaction than the other group.

The warm participants were also more likely to be generous with their colleagues, suggesting a relationship between trust and physical comfort.

Our brain cannot differentiate between physical and psychological sensations, so we interpret physical warmth and psychological warmth in the same way. We need to remember this when we are shaking someone's hand.

Can we really *manage* millennials?

Generation Y, also known as the *millennial generation* (those aged between approximately 19 and 35), is now the largest generation at work.

But differences in working styles between millennials and previous generations are creating some frustration on both sides. To these previous generations, millennials do not appear to share the same work ethic or loyalty. In fact a 2016 Gallup survey has reported that half of the millennial workforce does not see a future with their current organisation and that, in 2015, millennials changed jobs three times more frequently than non-millennials.[19] Gallup has estimated that this millennial turnover costs the United States economy $30.5 billion annually.

Millennials on the other hand feel that the 'entitled and lazy' labels that are often applied to them are unfair and untrue. Admittedly their concept of authority is different; in their view managers exert too much control, are too slow and are not plugged into technology. Having lived through a tough recession and having witnessed their parents cope with redundancy and job insecurity, millennials believe that they are entrepreneurial and resilient, but may not feel a strong sense of organisational allegiance.

The irony is that previous generations, such as the baby boomers who are struggling with their younger colleagues, are perhaps the very same people who have created this issue in the first place. Even though baby boomers have grown up with the regimen of a hierarchy and possible stricter parenting, they have in turn loosened their parental controls and granted millennials more freedom to make decisions and choices.

The millennial world is flat, equal and instant. Rewards have been plentiful, though often devalued by their frequency and separation from achievement; relationships are faster to build but more fragile and short-term; the immediacy of responses, often via social media, feeds an impatience and ever-worsening technological addiction.

And so, in a world where we have all become increasingly accustomed to having everything *now*, many millennials expect to enjoy a fast-track, obstacle-free career trajectory that quickly grants a high level of capability and success.

But, as Simon Sinek said in a recent interview:

'What they don't see is the mountain. I don't care whether you go up the mountain quickly or slowly. But there is still a mountain.'

In some businesses, the millennial turnover rate has prompted a recall of retired employees in order to retain accumulated knowledge. This makes sense for those organisations wishing to hold on to their intellectual capital, acquired skills, corporate heritage and organisational culture. It seems to be a more logical step than investing in the younger generations who cannot commit to the longer term.

It is clear that new thinking is needed about how to deal with millennials.

Some organisations have introduced new initiatives, such as programmes titled 'Managing Millennials', which are aimed at merging generations together into a more workable solution.

But perhaps trying to shoehorn millennials into a traditional, hierarchical way of working is not the answer. Alternative approaches have been implemented by some organisations, which are described later in this chapter.

The Toyota Production System involves all employees in the organisation – sales and marketing, administration, product development and management.

Toyota employees at every level have to learn the detail of each process in order to maintain the smooth operation of the company. This learning of detail is supported by the concept of the five Ss:

SEIRI   – **Sifting**
SEITON   – **Sorting**
SEISO   – **Sweeping and cleaning**
SEIKETSU   – **Spick-and-span**
SHITSUKE   – **Sustain**

Daily meetings are held at each plant to give people the opportunity to discuss problems, improvements and decisions. Toyota employees are therefore constantly working and hard-wiring these behaviours in the fabric of their brains.

Leadership is also about learning

The role of leadership should not be viewed as solely giving answers or setting direction, goals or objectives. Effective leaders are also learners who themselves facilitate learning in others.

We are far more engaged in a task when we are given the space and freedom to accomplish it for ourselves – and we are motivated on an intrinsic level. Learning to work with other people and solve problems collectively are skills that become hard-wired in our brains.

But time is always the problem

 Most leaders will claim that they know what to do in theory, but that they do not have the time to put new ideas into practice. It is often the case that tried-and-tested methods are familiar, comfortable, easy and quick, and therefore a lot more attractive than the prospect of trying something new.

And because we love feeling that we are solving problems quickly and efficiently, we keep doing it and our brain never has time to rest. The result is that, as pressures mount and change accelerates, we are stripped of the very same cognitive skills that are needed to meet these challenges.

If leaders are to create a working environment that gets the best out of their own brains and the brains of those they lead, it is more important than ever that a balance is found between activity and reflection. The faster we are expected and want to work, the more imperative it is that we find some moments of peace and calm.

The irony is that the more we resist taking regular breaks, the more we actually need them.

Attitudes are contagious

 Attitudes are contagious. Leaders should always question what kind of contagion their attitude brings to their environment and people. A leader's behaviour is constantly under scrutiny and being judged by those observing it.

A motivated workforce depends almost entirely on how motivated the leaders themselves appear.

However, because of the strong influence of our negativity bias, leaders need to keep reinforcing the positive in their communication, behaviour and practices. Positive emotions promote energy, counteract depression and anxiety, increase overall resilience and foster deeper connections with others.

The smallest act of kindness can make the biggest difference to other people.

Part 3: Stories and top tips

Manage millennials? Get them to mentor YOU instead!

Rather than *manage* millennials, some organisations have decided instead to harness the different skills millennials bring to the working environment. Our digital age, with its associated demands, now requires new operational and learning paradigms.

Enter *reverse mentoring*. This is an initiative that originated in 1999, when the CEO of General Electric at the time, Jack Welch, instructed his senior leaders to find a junior mentor to teach them computer skills.

UnitedHealth Group, headquartered in Minneapolis, has implemented a reverse-mentoring programme pairing eight senior executives in its insurance division with eight millennials – with an average age gap of 25 years.

The intention is that this programme will help executives look at the business differently and so help to prepare the working environment for the future.

PricewaterhouseCoopers, Cisco, Facebook, Microsoft and Procter & Gamble are among the companies that are following suit.

Today, some baby boomer leaders are similarly using the millennial generation to mentor their employees so that they can better understand rapid technological advances and social media opportunities.

Not surprisingly, the reverse-mentoring initiative is not widespread. For many senior executives, the prospect of learning from somebody younger and less experienced is anathema. However, the initiative is a great opportunity for people on either side of a generational gap to learn from each other, engage in a dialogue on an informal basis and view the world through the other's lens.

Perhaps the real answer here is in not labelling *millennials*, thereby creating an out-group (see Chapter 7, Our Brain and Biases). If we all see ourselves as belonging to the same group of working professionals, we may be able to work more effectively together.

Should we get rid of the performance appraisal?

Chapter 5, Our Brain and Language, discusses the format and content of the performance appraisal in detail, and offers some suggestions about how to construct more effective feedback conversations.

From a leadership perspective, the annual performance appraisal is a good example of a Theory X practice that may well have had its day. Results from a recent Corporate Executive Board (CEB) survey highlight that 95% of managers are dissatisfied with their performance appraisal process, 90% of human resources heads claim they do not yield accurate information, and 80% of global organisations are considering major changes to their performance appraisal systems.[20]

There are a number of reasons why the conventional performance appraisal does not work:

» The appraisal discussion is typically structured around the *feedback sandwich:* positive – negative – positive, which does not work well with our brain's natural negativity bias.

» The appraisal discussion often uncovers the bias and the attitude of the appraiser rather than the person being appraised.

» Leaders will often avoid difficult performance conversations until such time as the conversation can be positioned and protected by the formality of the annual discussion. They then shower the employee with feedback that can feel like an onslaught. Of course our brain will respond immediately to this and move into *fight or flight* mode.

» Appraisers often focus on most recent performance and do not take into account a more overall view. The attention paid to past performance and not future potential does not really engender an appetite to learn and look ahead.

» Many organisations are still using a rating system that was introduced in the 1970s to define human performance. This system ranks people on a 1–3 or 1–5 scale, with the lowest number or highest number denoting an outstanding performer and a problem employee being at the other end of the scale. The problem with this is that many leaders opt for the middle ground as it feels like the safest option: anything else needs to be justified or explained. In an attempt to distribute the scores more evenly, a forced ranking is often introduced.

General Electric became famous for this with their policy of having to rank certain individuals across the board and then let go of their bottom 10% (*rank and yank*). The problem with this forced ranking is that it feels exactly that: forced. And over time, it can backfire; when all the poor performers have been removed, the better performers are forced into the bottom percentile. So organisations may end up losing the people they actually do not want to lose.

» Academics and business professionals alike have spoken out against any system that uses a numerical rating as a means of evaluating performance. The use of a scale that positions people relatively against others can make them feel dehumanised and disadvantaged: their *status* is compromised and they do not view the process as *fair* – two basic human needs, as explained earlier.

In 2013, a study looked at how different kinds of people react to negative feedback.[21]

Two hundred university employees were asked to rate how they felt about a recent performance evaluation; they were also asked questions about their personal goals. The researchers hypothesised that those who were more learning-oriented would benefit from a performance review.

The study found, however, that all employees, even those with stated learning goals and aspirations, disliked the performance reviews.

As a consequence, the annual review is now being replaced in some organisations by a more realistic and accurate system, based on both the immediacy and the frequency of feedback.

Examples of organisations who have adopted new performance appraisal processes

» In 2012, Adobe replaced its evaluations process on the basis that it was unpopular and ineffective. Under the old system, leaders focused on the past instead of directing people towards the future. Now Adobe has introduced a more informal process that works on the basis of continual and real-time feedback.

» Microsoft redesigned its entire approach to appraising performance in 2013. It now focuses evaluation on results that people deliver together, leveraging and contributing to one another, emphasising continual learning and growth.

» Accenture introduced a new process in 2015 that rejects forced ranking and is instead using an app to facilitate regular feedback.

Promote a culture of learning

At Google, employees have always set their own goals. Google leaders also focus on helping people learn – by encouraging them to learn from each other.

A programme called Googler to Googler enables employees to teach each other a wide variety of skills. Conceived by

Chade-Meng Tan, an engineer at Google who started teaching mindfulness classes in the organisation, this initiative has enabled over 2,000 Google employees to teach over half of the company's education programmes across a workforce of 37,000 people.

Google's culture of learning means that Google employees also begin to promote the same philosophy themselves. Learning and helping others learn are disciplines that are now embedded in the way that Google people work together.

And so, if leaders promote a culture of collaborative learning, self-direction and self-discovery, people are more likely to strive for higher levels of success and achieve greater satisfaction and fulfilment.

A good culture brings out the best in all of us.

> **'The real role of leadership is climate control, creating a climate of possibility.'**
>
> **Sir Ken Robinson**

Transform people's performance through regular feedback and ongoing support. Show people that you are also learning and that you are open to receiving feedback. Consider adopting new approaches that appreciate and reward desired behaviour.

Respect people's need for status, certainty, autonomy, relatedness and fairness. Create a positive working environment. As a leader, you can influence how people treat each other, communicate, work and learn together.

Unite people behind a common purpose and encourage them to focus on this. Focus is critical to building new neural networks and positive habits over time. Limit distractions and interruptions, especially in meetings. Promote high standards of performance and behaviour.

Set people breaks. Longer hours do not make us more productive. In fact, studies show that people who work long hours tend to be less effective.[22] Regular breaks increase productivity and encourage new thinking, and reflection and thought are critical to cognitive agility. Our brain needs time out and it always works best when it is relaxed and happy.

Touch people in an inspirational way. Be a positive contagion in your environment. This requires a high level of self-knowledge and self-reflection. Your actions will speak louder than words ever will. Whatever you do as a leader will be noticed and replicated.

References for Chapter 11

1 The Global Workforce Leadership Survey (2015) *Workplace Trends* [trends.com]

2 Society for Human Resource Management, *Business and Human Capital Challenges Today and in the Future* (2015), 9 December [shrm.org]

3 Waltman, D.A. et al. (2011) 'Leadership and neuroscience: can we revolutionize the way that inspirational leaders are identified and developed?', *Academy of Management*, February, 60–74

4 Heisel, A.D. & M.J. Beatty (2006) 'Are cognitive representations of friends' request refusals implemented in the orbitofrontal and dorsolateral prefrontal cortices? A cognitive neuroscience approach to "theory of mind" in relationships', *Journal of Social and Personal Relationships*, April, 249–65

5 Salloway, S. et al. (2001) *The Frontal Lobes and Neuropsychiatric Illness*, Arlington, VA: American Psychiatric Association Publishing

6 Goleman, D. (1996) *Emotional Intelligence*. London: Bloomsbury

7 McGregor, D. (2006) *The Human Side of Enterprise*. New York: McGraw-Hill

8 Rosenthal, R. & S.L. Jacobson (1966) 'What you see is what you get. Teachers' expectancies: determinates of pupils' IQ gains', *Psychological Reports*, August, 115–18

9 Olivero, G. et al. (1997) 'Executive coaching as a transfer of training tool: effects on productivity in a public agency', *Public Personnel Management*, Summer, 341–56

10 Freeman, J. et al. (2015) 'Static and dynamic cues differentially affect the consistency of social evaluations', *Personality and Social Psychology Bulletin*, [doi.org/10.1177/0146167215591495]

11 Davila-Ross, M. et al. (2015) 'Chimpanzees (Pan troglodytes) produce the same types of "laugh faces" when they emit laughter and when they are silent', *PLOS ONE* [doi.org/10.1371/journal.pone.0127337]

12 McNally, L. et al. (2012) 'Cooperation and the evolution of intelligence', *Proceedings of the Royal Society B: Biological Sciences* [doi.org/10.1098/rspb.2012.0206]

13 Eisenberger, N. (2012) 'The neural bases of social pain: evidence for shared representations with physical pain', *Psychosomatic Medicine*, February, 126–35

14 Sapolsky, R. (2004) 'Social status and health in humans and other animals', *Annual Review of Anthropology*, June, 393–418

15 Rock, D. (2009) *Your Brain at Work: Strategies for Overcoming Distraction, Regaining Focus, and Working Smarter All Day Longer.* New York: HarperCollins

16 *Business Insider* (2013) 'The science of how temperature and lighting affect your productivity', 3 April [businessinsider.com]

17 Münch, M. et al. (2012) 'Effects of prior light exposure on early evening performance, subjective sleepiness, and hormonal secretion', *Behavioral Neuroscience*, February, 196–203

18 Williams, L.E. & J.A. Bargh (2008) 'Experiencing physical warmth promotes interpersonal warmth', *Science*, October, 606–07

19 Adkins, A. (2016) 'What millennials want from work and life', *Gallup Business Journal*, 11 May [gallup.com]

20 Corporate Executive Board (2013) Human Resources Business Partner Survey, 27 July [cebglobal.com]

21 Culbertson, S. et al. (2013) 'Performance appraisal satisfaction', *Journal of Personnel Psychology*, 12 (4) [doi.org/10.1027/1866-5888/a000096]

22 Staples Advantage 2015 Workplace Index [staplesadvantage.com]

'We are what we repeatedly do. Excellence, then, is not an act but a habit.'

Aristotle

Philosopher and scientist
(384–322 BC)

12: OUR BRAIN AND LIFESTYLE

The beginning of this book refers to the fact that we are hampered by our own evolution, and many of us struggle with the pressures of keeping up with constant change and disruption.

But the speed of our digital world means that much of our time is now spent . . . sitting down!

The problems associated with our sedentary lifestyle are exacerbated by a lack of sleep and a poor diet. Many of us are compromising our long-term health, the negative effects of which are receiving increasing attention on the part of scientists, researchers and business executives.

This final chapter explores our modern lifestyle and suggests ways in which we can maintain well-functioning brains and bodies. The three areas of lifestyle covered are sleep, physical exercise and food.

Part 1: The science explained

Our brain and sleep

Sleep is essential for brain health

We spend a third of our life asleep. Sleep plays a vital role in maintaining our health and wellbeing. During sleep, our brain is very active and works hard to maintain our physical and mental health.

A good night's sleep improves the way we learn and think. We also benefit from increased energy, a more robust immune system, sharper concentration, better decision-making and improved physical health.

 From a neurological point of view, sleep consolidates our neural pathways by strengthening our memories and repairing our cells.

For children, a deep sleep enables the release of growth hormone and promotes muscle development.

How do we go to sleep?

Our *neurotransmitters*, or brain chemicals, control whether we are asleep or awake. When we feel tired, two main neurotransmitters are involved in helping us go to sleep: *melatonin* and *adenosine*. Although research is still trying to uncover the precise role of these chemicals in sleep, our current understanding is that the build-up of both melatonin and adenosine in our body will make us feel drowsy.

Melatonin and adenosine normally peak together around 9pm, telling the body that we need to sleep.

» **Melatonin**
   Melatonin is released when our environment gets dark and switches off when it gets light again. The build-up of melatonin makes us want to go to sleep. This is why having a light switched on in the bedroom – even a light from an electronic device – may interfere with sleep.

» **Adenosine**
   Adenosine accumulates when we are awake. The more adenosine we have, the sleepier we feel. Sleep will lower our adenosine levels, but if we do not then get enough sleep, the remaining adenosine in our body will make us tired. We may then need to sleep longer the following night to purge any excess adenosine.

Caffeine interferes with the accumulation of adenosine and as a result gives us more energy.

The stages of sleep

We have two types of sleep: *non-REM* and *REM* (rapid eye movement).

1) Non-REM sleep

We experience non-REM when we first go to sleep. There are four stages of non-REM sleep.

» **Stage one: light sleep**
We drift in and out of sleep and can be awakened easily.
Our eyes move very slowly and muscle activity slows.
As we enter sleep, our body may twitch involuntarily and
experience a *hypnic* or *hypnagogic jerk*, which gives us a
strange sense of falling. Scientists are divided as to why we
do this: some claim that it is a final attempt by the brain to
hold on to daytime motor control, while others say that this
experience is a hangover reflex from more primitive days
when we may have had to prevent ourselves from falling
from a tree.

» **Stage two: sleep spindles**
Our brainwaves now slow down, although there are still
occasional bursts of rapid waves called *sleep spindles*.
We spend the majority of our sleep in Stage two. Sleep
spindles refresh our brain, particularly in the hippocampus
and the prefrontal cortex, areas that are essential for
learning. The greater the number of sleep spindles we
have, the better our cognitive functioning.[1]

» **Stage three: deep sleep (1)**
Our brainwaves now become extremely slow. These are
known as *delta waves* and they are interspersed with
smaller, faster waves.

» **Stage four: deep sleep (2)**
The brain now only produces delta waves, which is what
we call deep sleep. During this stage, we have no eye
movement or muscle activity. If we are awakened during
deep sleep, we cannot adjust immediately and often feel
disorientated for several minutes.

Sleepwalking, whereby a person walks or may even perform
complex behaviours while asleep, normally originates during

deep sleep. Sleepwalking is more common in children than adults and is normally the result of sleep deprivation. It is very difficult to wake someone up during this stage of sleep.

2) REM sleep

We move into REM sleep approximately 90 minutes after falling asleep. REM sleep then occurs in cycles of between 90 and 120 minutes during the night.

This stage of sleep is when we dream and our brain speeds up and becomes very active. Our breathing also quickens and our eyes jerk rapidly in various directions (hence the name rapid eye movement).

During this stage, the muscles in our limbs become temporarily paralysed to prevent us from acting out our dreams. If we awaken during REM sleep, we often remember our dreams.

Figure 12.1: The alternating stages of non-REM and REM sleep

REM sleep may be reduced by antidepressants or smoking. Heavy smokers may find that nicotine withdrawal causes them to wake up every three or four hours during the night.

Alcohol may also affect our sleep quality and prevent us from accessing deep sleep.

Sleep cleans our brain

One of the most important functions of sleep is to clean our brain and remove the toxins that build up during the day.[2] Our brain's cleaning system is known as the *glymphatic system*. This system involves the flow of cerebrospinal fluid, which surrounds our brain and spinal cord, through our brain. The glymphatic system is similar to our *lymphatic network* of glands, which filters waste out of our body. In our brain we have a specialised network that relies on *glial cells* (hence *glymphatic*), which support and supply nutrients to our neurons.

When we sleep, cerebrospinal fluid moves more quickly through our brain than when we are awake, thereby flushing out any toxins or waste more effectively.

One of these toxins, *beta-amyloid*, is known to accumulate in the brains of patients suffering from Alzheimer's Disease.

Sleep may therefore have an important role to play in the prevention or delay of dementia.

Our body clock

The biological changes that occur during the day are known as *circadian* (from the Latin meaning 'around a day') *rhythms*.

These rhythms are controlled by our body clock, which is in the brain and is called the *suprachiasmatic nucleus* (SCN), situated near the hypothalamus in the temporal lobe.

Figure 12.2: Our SCN, or body clock

The SCN plays an important role in our sleep/wake cycle and governs our body temperature, hormonal release and blood pressure.

When light enters the eye, signals travel along the optic nerve to the SCN and then on to several brain regions, including the pineal gland, which switches off melatonin. This is what makes us drowsy at night.

Our circadian rhythms normally follow the 24-hour clock and we feel more awake or sleepy at certain periods during the day (see Figure 12.3).

These rhythms are disrupted when we travel across time zones, causing jet lag. It can take several days to reset our body clock and resume normal sleeping patterns.

A recent study has suggested that just a weekend camping is an effective way to reset our body clock since it encourages us to be more aligned with the natural light/dark cycle.[3]

Figure 12.3: Our circadian rhythms

How much sleep do we need?

Scientists continue to debate how much sleep we need and how this amount will vary throughout our lifetime.

A review of scientific literature across the world has recently been conducted to consider how the amount of sleep we get relates to performance, health and safety. Based on this review, we now have the first recommended age-specific sleep ranges for most age groups, as detailed in Figure 12.4.[4]

Age	Sleep range (hours per day)
Newborns (0–3 months)	14–17
Infants (4–11 months)	12–15
Toddlers (1–2 years)	11–14
Pre-schoolers (3–5 years)	10–13
School-age children (6–13 years)	9–11
Teenagers (14–17 years)	8–10
Younger adults (18–25 years)	7–9
Adults (26–64 years)	7–9
Older adults (65+ years)	7–8

Figure 12.4: Recommended sleep ranges

Why do teenagers need more sleep than adults?

Teenagers may follow a slightly different circadian rhythm since adolescence causes a sleep phase delay. Teenagers' melatonin levels rise later at night than in other age groups, making it difficult for them to fall asleep before 11pm.

This sleep phase delay can result in sleep deprivation because they are still expected to wake up for school. It is therefore important to keep the lights dim in the evening to encourage melatonin production at night and then to switch it off by bringing light into the room as soon as possible in the morning. And, of course, we should remove all electronic devices, which are potentially distracting.

The importance of alpha waves before sleep

When we are awake, our two dominant brainwaves are *beta* and *alpha waves*:

» **Beta waves**
These waves are active when we are thinking, reading, working or talking.

» **Alpha waves**
These waves help the brain to slow down and relax. They also occur during the early stages of meditation.

Our brain normally maintains a healthy balance between beta and alpha waves. If we have too many beta waves, we find it hard to relax, while too many alpha waves can slow us down too much.

Because our alpha waves are relaxing, they are often the gateway to sleep. The main benefits of alpha waves are that they help us to relax and they slow down our heart rate. This gives our body a chance to recover and helps to consolidate our learning and memory.

Different types of insomnia

Insomnia is a condition that prevents us either going to sleep or staying asleep. There are different types of insomnia.

Acute insomnia	Occurs for brief periods and is usually caused by short-term stress such as bad news, travel or a change in our life. Normally, acute insomnia resolves itself without any need for treatment.
Chronic insomnia	Longer-term issue where we find it difficult either to fall asleep or stay asleep for at least three nights a week over a period of three or more months. There are a number of causes of chronic insomnia, some of which are described later in this chapter.
Comorbid insomnia	Occurs with another condition, such as depression or any pain in the body that makes it hard for us to sleep.
Onset insomnia	We have difficulty falling asleep.
Maintenance insomnia	We cannot stay asleep and we often wake up during the night. This occurs typically when we cross time zones.

What causes insomnia?

There are various causes of insomnia. A number of medical conditions, such as nasal or sinus problems, indigestion, arthritis, back pain or Parkinson's Disease can all lead to insomnia.

Other disorders linked to insomnia are:

» **Depression**
Worsened by insomnia.

» **Anxiety**
We worry about past and future events. One can worsen the other.

» **Restless legs syndrome**
An uncomfortable urge to move the legs.

» **Sleep apnoea**
The airways become obstructed and oxygen levels drop.

Treatment for insomnia

If we are having problems sleeping, we need to address these. Poor sleep should not become a way of life!

It is always a good idea to examine our sleep habits and ensure that we are creating an environment conducive to a good night's sleep. Healthier sleep habits are critical to a healthy lifestyle.

For example, we should ensure that our bedroom is dark to stimulate the production of melatonin, and cool to compensate for our rise in body temperature during the night. We should also have no distractions around us, such as our mobile telephone or computer.

Why does lack of sleep make us hungry?

Sleep helps to keep our hormones in balance, and lack of sleep can upset this balance very quickly. *Ghrelin* is a hormone that makes us feel hungry, while *leptin* is a hormone that indicates we have had enough to eat and helps the body maintain its weight.

A lack of sleep causes increased levels of ghrelin and decreased levels of leptin, causing us to feel hungry. This is why when we are jet-lagged, we crave high-energy foods such as carbohydrates.

Figure 12.5: A lack of sleep makes us hungry

Why do we dream?

Dreams are effectively images that we experience when we are asleep. Our most vivid dreams occur during REM sleep, when our brain is most active. Some experts say we dream at least four to six times per night.

Dreaming is important to our health and wellbeing. Studies have found that when we are not allowed to dream we experience more anxiety, depression, concentration and coordination problems. Alcohol and drugs affect the REM cycle and therefore our dreams.

So why do some of us regularly remember our dreams while others are unable to recall anything?

This question has been investigated by researchers who have discovered a specific brain region for encoding and remembering dreams.[5]

Using positron emission tomography (PET), researchers measured the brain activity of two groups of people during wakefulness and sleep:

Group 1: People who remember their dreams five days a week on average

Group 2: People who remember their dreams twice a month on average

In both wakefulness and sleep, the first group showed higher activity in two areas of the brain (*medial prefrontal cortex* and the *temporo-parietal junction*) that are responsible for paying attention to external stimuli – in particular, sound.

This study supports earlier brain research showing that damage to these regions can result in no dream recall whatsoever.

And so it seems that the more sensitive we are to what is going on around us when we are awake, the more likely we are to recall what happens to us when we are asleep.

Our brain and physical exercise

The brain is a muscle

Our brain is like every other muscle in our body, in that we need to exercise it to keep it fit and healthy. While mental activities are good for our brain, physical exercise has an even more positive effect on brain function.

Even exercising for 20 minutes is beneficial for our brain health.[6] Exercise reduces our resistance to insulin, making it easier for us to break down sugars in our body. Exercise also reduces inflammation and stimulates the production of chemicals that maintain the health and survival of our brain cells.

A 2016 study found that schizophrenia patients who engaged in physical activity improved their cognitive function and quality of life. [7]

Exercise grows our brain . . .

Our brain uses 20% of all the oxygen in our body. When we exercise, we increase our heart rate, which in turn pumps more oxygen to our brain. In fact, it is regular aerobic exercise of moderate intensity, rather than low-impact alternatives, that enlarges the size of the hippocampus which is specifically involved in memory and learning.[8]

This is an important finding because the hippocampus is also the area of the brain affected by dementia. Researchers say one new case of dementia is detected globally every four seconds. They estimate that by the year 2050 more than 115 million people worldwide will have dementia. Alzheimer's Disease is now the number one killer in the United Kingdom.

Physical exercise also leads to a higher concentration of growth factors in the brain, which makes it easier for our brain to grow new connections.[9] Studies are now pointing to other brain regions that show increased volume through exercise, such as the *prefrontal cortex* and *medial temporal cortex*. These areas are both important for the formation and consolidation of memories.[10]

. . . and even reverses signs of ageing

 Although our brain growth slows as we age and our brain starts to shrink, exercise may nevertheless prevent or even reverse this trend. Six months of aerobic exercise has been found to increase brain volume and reduce age-related brain changes in a group of people aged between 60 and 79.

Regular exercise by adults in this age group, even after as few as four weeks, has also been shown to cause an increase in cognitive ability.

Exercise alleviates symptoms of depression

Studies have shown that running has an antidepressant effect on our brain.[11] If patients suffering from depression exercise for five days a week over three months, they can reduce their symptoms by half.[12]

Regular exercise also releases endorphins (the word *endorphin* is derived from the words *endogenous morphine*, which is our internally produced painkiller) and increases our body's temperature. This has a calming effect and also reduces *cortisol*, the hormone we produce when we are stressed.

Exercise may not be the only treatment for depression, but it is certainly an effective means of reducing many of the symptoms people experience.

Exercise helps us to sleep

Because exercise reduces stress and makes us tired, it may help to regulate our body clock so that we sleep more effectively. Outdoor exercise during daytime is particularly beneficial because we absorb natural sunlight.

The time of day that we exercise will vary for each of us and will depend on our *chronotype*, which refers to our personal biological clock or natural preference for going to sleep or when we feel at our most alert and energetic. For example, some of us may prefer to exercise in the morning, while others prefer the evening.

We often refer to our chronotype when we say, 'I am/am not a morning person', which is discussed later in this chapter.

Our brain and food

What food is best for our brain?

Increasingly, we are flooded with recommendations for food that we should and should not be eating for the sake of our health. But it seems that in among all the advice and warnings there are some foods that all scientists agree are good for our brain.

As already mentioned, omega-3 is very beneficial for our brain function, facilitating communication between neurons and repairing damage. Omega-3 is particularly important in maintaining a healthy *myelin sheath*, the fatty substance that insulates our nerve fibres and enables proper functioning of our nervous system.

Omega-3 is an essential fatty acid (EFA) that cannot be made by the body so we need to obtain it through what we eat. The quality of our brain cells depends on the availability of EFAs. Sources of EFAs include linseed (flaxseed), soya beans, pumpkin seeds, walnuts and their oils.

Omega-3 fats occur naturally in oily fish (salmon, trout, mackerel, herring, sardines, pilchards and kippers) in the form of EPA (eicosapentaenoic acid) and DHA (docosahexaenoic acid), which are the most important group of nutrients for our brain. Most modern diets do not provide enough omega-3 fats and it is estimated that 70% of us do not get enough. Low DHA levels have been linked to an increased risk of Alzheimer's Disease and memory loss.

Other recommended foods include:

» Blackcurrants (vitamin C) – to increase cognitive agility.

» Blueberries (vitamins K and C) – to improve memory, reduce DNA damage and slow cognitive decline.

» Broccoli (vitamin K, choline and folic acid) – to strengthen cognitive abilities and memory consolidation.

» Chicken, turkey, eggs and soya beans (vitamin B6) – to enhance cognitive performance and raise mood.

» Lamb, beef, feta and cottage cheese (vitamin B12) – to protect against brain shrinkage (especially in the elderly).

» Nuts (vitamin E and DHA) – to support brain health, protect neurons and prevent cognitive decline.

» Pumpkin seeds (zinc, magesium and B vitamins) – to boost memory, focus and cognitive function.

» Sage (vitamin A, calcium and magnesium) – to improve memory and concentration.

» Tomatoes (carotenoids, calcium and vitamins A, C and K) – to eliminate free radical damage that occurs in dementia.

The link between mood and food

Mood and food are definitely connected. Our *neurotransmitters* regulate our mood, while our food affects the regulation of our neurotransmitters. Proteins help us to manufacture amino acids – chemicals that are converted to neurotransmitters to help regulate our mood. Our brain is about 70% fat and it particularly needs omega-3s (found in oily fish, as mentioned above) for brain development and for moderating our moods and behaviour, even to the extent of aiding in easing depression and lowering suicide risk.[13]

We need to maintain the right balance of neurotransmitters. Our food intake affects this balance, as Figure 12.6 illustrates.

Neurotransmitter: Serotonin

Related amino acid	Role	Some symptoms of deficiency	Food
Tryptophan	Inhibitory neuro-transmitter. Plays an important role in regulating mood, happiness, relaxation, appetite, memory, bowel function, learning and hormonal release.	Depressed mood, anxiety, panic attacks, low energy, sleeping problems, feeling tense and irritable, impaired memory and concentration.	Fish, eggs, chicken, turkey and other meats. Iron, zinc. Vitamins B3, B6 and C.

Neurotransmitter: Dopamine

Related amino acid	Role	Some symptoms of deficiency	Food
Tyrosine	Both excitatory and inhibitory neuro-transmitter. Responsible for movement, memory, pleasurable reward, attention, desire and drive to get things done. Known as our *motivation molecule*. Controls movement and posture.	Memory problems, poor concentration, difficulty initiating or completing tasks, lack of energy, lack of motivation, addictions, cravings, compulsions, a loss of satisfaction and libido. Too little dopamine is implicated in Parkinson's Disease.	Almonds, avocados, dairy products, pumpkin and sesame seeds. Folic acid, vitamin B6, magnesium and zinc.

Neurotransmitter: Glutamate

Related amino acid	Role	Some symptoms of deficiency	Food
Glutamate/ Glutamic acid	Major excitatory neurotransmitter in our brain. Involved in cognition, memory and learning.	Insomnia, problems concentrating, mental exhaustion and depleted energy.	Cured meats, aged cheese, soy sauce and soy protein, mushrooms, ripe tomatoes, broccoli, peas, walnuts, grape juice.

Neurotransmitter: GABA

Related amino acid	Role	Some symptoms of deficiency	Food
Glutamine Taurine Theanine	Inhibitory neurotransmitter. GABA (gamma-amino butyric acid) acts as a natural sedative and tranquilliser and calms nervous activity. Contributes to motor control and vision.	Anxiety disorders, racing thoughts, bipolar disorder, mania, poor impulse control, panic attacks, cold hands, shortness of breath.	Halibut, mackerel, legumes, brown rice, wheat, bran, bananas, spinach. Vitamins B3, B6 and B12.

Neurotransmitter: Acetylcholine

Related amino acid	Role	Some symptoms of deficiency	Food
Choline	Widely distributed excitatory neurotransmitter. Major impact on wakefulness, attentiveness and arousal. Needed to turn short-term memories into long-term ones. Released to activate muscles. (Botox is a neurotoxin that blocks the effect of acetylcholine, preventing the facial muscles from moving.)	Low energy levels, memory loss, learning problems, muscle aches, cognitive decline. People with Alzheimer's Disease have altered levels of acetylcholine. Also implicated in Parkinson's Disease.	Almonds, blueberries, cruciferous vegetables, cheese, eggs, fish, chicken. Vitamin B6.

Neurotransmitter: Noradrenaline

Related amino acid	Role	Some symptoms of deficiency	Food
Tyrosine	Excitatory neurotransmitter. Triggers changes in the body in response to stress (increased oxygen, heart rate and glucose) to raise our alertness and *fight or flight* capacity. Important for attentiveness, emotions, dreaming and learning.	Depression, loss of alertness, memory problems, lack of energy, focus and motivation.	Almonds, avocados, dairy products, pumpkin and sesame seeds. Folic acid, vitamin B6, magnesium and zinc.

Figure 12.6: Neurotransmitters, amino acids and food

Part 2: Impact on our daily life

Our brain and sleep

We need to sleep

All of us need to sleep. The longer we have been awake, the stronger our desire to sleep. The longer we have been asleep, the more the pressure to sleep reduces.

But we are an arrogant species and we think we can override our body clock and beat sleep. Many of us are either not aware of the risks of sleep deficiency or we choose to ignore the signs. We believe that we can survive on a few hours of sleep a night and still function efficiently. In fact, we often do not even realise that we are suffering from lack of sleep.

Studies show that our ability to drive a car is as much affected by lack of sleep as if we were under the influence of alcohol. In addition, lack of sleep can cause an increase in hyperactivity and can affect our ability to focus on tasks – symptoms that are very similar to attention deficit hyperactivity disorder (ADHD).

What is the impact of sleep deficiency?

Sleep deficiency can be fatal. Even one night without sleep will have a significant impact on our brain and body. When we continually do not have enough sleep, we can suffer from both health and cognitive problems that may impact our decisions, behaviour and relationships. Severe sleep deficiency can contribute towards mental health issues such as stress, depression, extreme risk-taking and even perhaps suicide. Physical issues associated with lack of sleep may also be increased, such as risk of stroke, obesity and heart problems.

Sleep deficiency can cause our blood sugar levels to rise, making us more at risk of diabetes. Our neurons may also become depleted in energy, affecting our immune system and leaving us vulnerable to infection and illness.

Shift work can be dangerous

Shift workers who work erratic hours against their natural body clock are more likely to suffer from conditions such as cardiovascular disease, breast cancer and digestive problems. Shift work can also prematurely age the brain by over six years.[14] Research has shown that medical interns on the night shift are more likely to misinterpret hospital test records than the interns working during the day.

In 1984, more than 40 tons of toxic gas leaked from a pesticide plant in Bhopal, India, killing thousands of people. More than 150 people were left severely disabled and 22,000 have since died of their injuries. This occurred during a night shift.

In 1986, the Chernobyl nuclear power plant went into meltdown, causing the deaths of thousands of people from radiation-related illnesses. The disaster was caused by a mistake during a night shift.

In 1989, the Exxon Valdez oil spill, during which 750,000 barrels of oil were spilt off the coast of Alaska, happened during a night shift.

Research has examined methods of reducing shift-work tiredness, including bright lights, shorter schedules and intermittent naps.

Even though the brain is affected by night-shift work, it can recover and return to regular function – but this can take over five years.

Why are power naps good for us?

 The power nap is being increasingly heralded as an effective way to boost our brain function. Power naps take us into Stages one and two of non-REM sleep and should ideally last for 20 to 30 minutes. Memory consolidation starts while we nap and this results in increased productivity, increased cognitive functioning, enhanced creativity and greater alertness.

However, if we nap too long we enter Stage three sleep and may feel more sleepy and disorientated if we are awakened during this stage.

So power naps can make us more productive and energetic and reboot our system, improving our cognitive ability and sensitivity to sensory input.[15] They also decrease our risk of cardiovascular disease.[16]

Are we larks or owls?

There is much debate about whether morning people (*larks*) are more effective than evening people (*owls*). As mentioned earlier in this chapter, the term for whether we are morning or evening people is our *chronotype*.

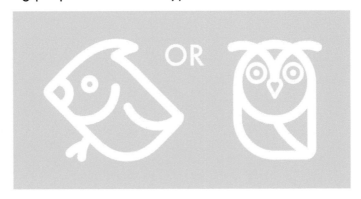

About 10% of people are true larks and 20% are true owls, with the majority of us somewhere in the middle. Most people claim to be at their peak performance at a certain time during the day. For larks this preference will be early morning and for owls it will be in the evening.

Research has been contradictory about which chronotype is more successful. Some studies claim that larks report higher levels of happiness, productivity and fulfilment than owls. This may be explained by larks reporting that they feel they have greater choice and control over their mornings, while owls claim to suffer from lower wellbeing, higher stress and lower physical activity.[17] One study has claimed that owls are less reliable and less emotionally stable,[18] more prone to depression and eating disorders, while another suggests that owls have higher IQs than larks.[19]

Whatever the research, it seems that culture plays a role in establishing our chronotype. For example, some cultures are constructed around evening activities, while others place more emphasis on daytime productivity. Of course difficulties then arise when people cross over from one culture to another and need to fit in with differences in timekeeping as well as different time zones.

As we learn more about how our brains operate, perhaps we should be questioning working practices and adapting our schedules to fit in with our chronotypes, in order that we can give the best of ourselves.

But regardless of chronotype, sleep is vital to the healthy functioning of our body and brain.

Our brain and physical exercise

Is sitting the new smoking?

We sit for longer than we sleep! But scientists are now telling us that sitting for longer than six hours a day could be as bad for us as smoking a packet of cigarettes.

The human body is not designed to sit for long periods. We expend no or very little energy when we sit.

A number of studies highlight the risks of sitting all day:

Men who were sedentary for more than 23 hours a week had a 64% greater risk of dying from heart disease than those who were sedentary fewer than 11 hours a week.[20]

General risk of mortality is 1.54 times higher among people who spend most of their day sitting, compared to those who sit infrequently.[21]

Sitting at the computer or in front of the television leads to weight gain and obesity.[22]

> Children who watch just one hour of television a day are 50 to 60% more likely to be overweight and 58 to 73% more likely to be obese, compared to children who watch less than an hour.[23]

To counteract the detrimental effects of sitting, we need to stand up every 30 minutes, walk around and move our muscles. If we wait for longer than an hour, our fat-burning enzymes decline by 90%.

Can we walk and work at the same time?

The risks of excessive sitting are clear. As a result, studies have been looking at the benefits of the standing or treadmill desk.

Standing desks are gaining in popularity in offices all over the world. But it seems that standing is just the start. Standing burns 50 more calories per hour, but to gain optimal benefits it is important to walk around too.[24]

Although there is still some debate about their definitive benefits, treadmill desks are now being linked to improved attention and short-term recall.[25] Participants in studies of these desks' cognitive effects have reported paying better attention than the sedentary control group.

An electroencephalogram (EEG), a test that detects electrical activity in our brain using small electrodes attached to the scalp, has also revealed increased brain function in the region associated with memory and attention in those using the treadmill desk.

Our brain and food

Stress either starves us or makes us fatter

Stress affects our appetite in various ways. Some of us eat less when we are stressed, while others eat more.

When we are stressed, we activate our fight-or-flight response, and increase our levels of adrenaline (*epinephrine*) and suppress calming neurotransmitters such as serotonin, which regulates mood. Lack of serotonin increases anxiety and reduces feelings of hunger.

On the other hand, eating may become a coping mechanism and a strategy to deal with stress in our life. We may reach for high-sugar foods that give us instant energy, and then become conditioned to eat and crave the wrong food every time we feel stressed or anxious. We may feel unhappy that we are eating too much, but this does not reduce the craving to eat – in fact we may want to eat even more!

The problem is that, if we gain weight through stress-induced eating, we are more likely to hyperventilate and suffer panic attacks. This in turn makes us crave the wrong food. So we need to break the cycle, ignore our instinctive response and understand that we have to work harder to maintain a healthy lifestyle when we are feeling stressed.

Qualified dieticians are a helpful resource when trying to establish the food that is best for your individual system and overall wellbeing.

Fat OR sugar – but not both!

There is no food in the natural world that combines both fat and sugar. In other words, our brain and body are not designed to eat cake or doughnuts! Research has shown that a combination of fat and sugar is so addictive that it could be one of the causes of today's obesity epidemic.

In a study with rats, one group was given a sugar-rich diet and another group was given fat.[26] Neither group of rats gained much weight on either diet. However, when fat and sugar were combined (in cheesecake) the reaction of the animals was completely different. The rats did not just eat the food – they binged on it, even when they should have been full, and gained massive amounts of weight.

While a rat on a fat-only diet might take nearly two months to gain a small amount of weight, the cheesecake-eating rats gained significant weight after just seven days. What was even more interesting was that, having eaten cheesecake, they showed absolutely no interest in healthy food afterwards, preferring to starve instead. They were even prepared to endure mild electric shocks to be able to eat the junk food, demonstrating that this had now become an addiction.

Is obesity linked to dementia?

For years, scientists have been reporting that being obese, at all ages, may be damaging the brain. In children as young as seven years old, studies have shown that obesity can lead to memory problems.[27]

A diet that is rich in sugar and fat causes inflammation of the hippocampus (the brain region involved in memory and learning) and consequent memory impairments.[28] The hippocampus is particularly sensitive to diet. If the hippocampus is damaged prior to weight gain, through eating foods high in saturated fat and refined sugar, it may then cause the brain to crave the very foods that caused the dysfunction in the first place. Obesity is therefore often the result of a negative, repetitive cycle.

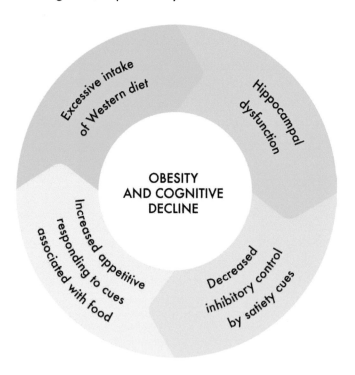

Figure 12.7: Obesity and cognitive decline – a vicious cycle

(Adapted from Davidson et al.[29])

Part 3: Stories and top tips

Sleep disorders are on the rise

With the proliferation of electronic devices across the world, we are now seeing an increase in sleep disorders in both children and adults.

Studies have highlighted the damaging effects of the blue light that emanates from laptops; it activates our SCN, or body clock, which in turn decreases melatonin, resulting in a lack of sleep.[30]

Teenagers are most at risk of sleep disorders because of their obsession with social networking and video games; this disturbs their sleep patterns at night and makes them more tired during the day.

Researchers suggest that over the last four decades the average total hours of sleep have decreased to less than seven hours per person per night.[31] The impact of this sleep deprivation is being linked to increased insulin resistance and higher numbers of people suffering from obesity and diabetes.

Both deep sleep and REM sleep are particularly important for our brain growth and development, particularly in young children. These stages of sleep help the brain to hold on to important information and get rid of useless detail, preparing the brain for a new day of input.

When we learn something, we build a web of synaptic connections that are then reorganised during REM sleep.

If we do not have enough REM sleep our brain is not refreshed, organised and ready to take in new information. As a consequence, we have problems focusing and learning the next day.

Sleep clinics are now looking at why children have trouble moving into deep delta sleep or REM sleep. Many teenagers are now sleep-deprived and get less than six hours' sleep at night. This lack of sleep, accompanied by higher levels of the hormone ghrelin, which makes us feel hungry, is also leading to more cases of obesity.

Teatime? Refuel in a sleep pod!

In response to growing research that extols the benefits of the power nap, a number of companies, including Google, Facebook, Procter & Gamble and NASA, are offering their workers sleeping pods. These pods offer a break in the middle of the working day – and they are timed for a 20-minute nap. So when energy levels drop at around 3pm, employees can refuel in a sleeping pod for 20 minutes. This power nap is reported as increasing alertness by around 30%.

Airports, including Abu Dhabi International, are now offering similar pods to people in transit, while many other companies are now capitalising on this trend.

For example, Arianna Huffington's *Huffington Post*, based in New York City, now has two rooms designated for power naps after Ms Huffington collapsed from exhaustion at her desk one night. Arianna Huffington is now a strong advocate of health and wellness at work.

Running our way to happiness

 For several years, a primary school in Stirling, Scotland, has made all its pupils walk or run a mile each day. The teachers at St Ninian's take their pupils out of lessons on to a specially built circuit around the school's playing field for their daily mile whenever it best suits that day's timetable. Only ice or very heavy rain results in a cancellation.

Not only are none of the children at the school overweight, despite the rise in childhood obesity across the United Kingdom, but their overall fitness, behaviour and concentration have also shown marked improvements. The children are also reported to be happy and productive in class.

The success of this scheme is so impressive that 500 other primary schools across the United Kingdom have adopted the *daily mile*. The interest that this scheme has generated has prompted Stirling University to set up a study to collect evidence of the daily mile's overall benefits to the children's physical, cognitive and emotional health.

Is clean eating a dangerous fad?

The pressures of social media, and in particular the *selfie*, have given rise to a growing obsession among teenagers with diets. *Clean eating* is a recent fad that has been linked to eating disorders, most particularly a fixation with strict rules about eating, which is becoming known as *orthorexia nervosa*. This is an eating disorder closely connected with *anorexia nervosa*, the mental illness with the highest mortality rate, and often starts as a desire to eat healthily and then becomes an obsession.

Cases of orthorexia are continuing to rise. The surge in *healthy food* bloggers, making links between weight loss and a desirable lifestyle, seems to have fuelled an obsession about dietary restrictions and limited food intake. This trend is not helped by the modern emphasis on self-publicity and lifestyle showcasing, with people comparing themselves unfavourably to the images that are promoted online.

But obsessive and restrictive eating habits lower energy and concentration levels, raise anxiety, and lead to an overall decline in physical health. A more beneficial approach is to eat with the right balance of nutrients, which enables us to live life to the full.

The 2016 documentary *Embrace* details the story of Taryn Brumfitt, who charts her own journey of self-discovery. Ms Brumfitt highlights the debilitating effects of poor body image. She explains why it is more important than ever to prioritise health over perceived beauty, and to be more accepting and appreciative of the body we have been given.

Are we drinking our way to death?

Much has been made over the years about the dangers of alcohol. Guidelines are published and updated regularly to encourage us to regulate our alcohol intake, and yet researchers have still not settled on one definitive rule. There are numerous studies that link moderate alcohol consumption with decreased risk of heart failure or stroke, and some studies even suggest that alcohol increases creativity.

There is no doubt that in many countries in the world alcohol plays a strong role as a social lubricant. And we are all different, which means that the effects of alcohol depend on a number of individual factors, such as age, metabolism and genetics. Men and women are also affected differently, and the 'safe' limits vary around the world. The United Kingdom has recently suggested no more than 14 units a week (six pints of beer), to be consumed over several days.

A World Health Organization fact sheet (updated in 2015) states that alcohol is a causal factor in over 200 disease and injury conditions, causing over three million deaths worldwide per year, equating to 5.9% of all deaths. Alcohol consumption is now also linked to tuberculosis, pneumonia and more than seven types of cancer. Alcohol currently sits alongside asbestos as a class 1 carcinogen. When our body breaks down alcohol it produces a chemical called acetaldehyde, which is strongly linked to cancer. Liver disease is another consequence of chronic alcohol consumption.

Interestingly, some people who drink in moderation exhibit lower cardiovascular risk than others who do not drink at all. This is probably due to the fact that moderate alcohol consumption, accompanied by regular exercise, sufficient sleep and a balanced diet, has a more beneficial effect than a sedentary lifestyle with no alcohol.

But this does not mean that exercise will nullify the effects of alcohol completely. While exercise may compensate for some of the damage associated with excessive alcohol consumption, a more worthy objective should be to maintain a healthy lifestyle overall.

Heal yourself through sleep. Pay attention to your sleep habits and compensate for lack of sleep as soon as possible. Sleep deficiency builds up like an overdraft in the bank – and we need to pay it back! Avoid caffeine from at least four hours before bedtime and keep evening meals light. Remove technological devices from the bedroom.

Avoid junk food and limit your intake of sugary and processed food that has little nutritional value. Instead, nourish your body with foods that are rich in protein, essential fats, vitamins and minerals. In stressful situations, increase your intake of magnesium and vitamin B12, which reduce anxiety and panic attacks.

Boost your heart rate on a regular basis. Standard recommendations advise half an hour of moderate physical activity most days of the week. Any exercise that increases our heart rate is beneficial, including household jobs or gardening. An oxygenated brain functions well.

Identify the stressors in your life. Stress is not good for us and can lead to lack of sleep and to eating the wrong foods. Find ways to develop healthy strategies to help deal with the pressures of life.

Think about your mood and state of mind. Make sure that you are developing strategies to create the right balance between motivation and relaxation. A balanced and nutritional diet will help promote greater calm and wellbeing. Focus on the positive aspects of your life.

References for Chapter 12

1 Walker, M.P. et al. (2007) 'The human emotional brain without sleep – a prefrontal amygdala disconnect', *Current Biology*, October, 877–78

2 Nedergaard, M. et al. (2012) 'A paravascular pathway facilitates CSF flow through the brain parenchyma and the clearance of interstitial solutes, including amyloid', *Science Translational Medicine*, August [doi.org/10.1126/scitranslmed.3003748]

3 Stothard, E.R. et al. (2017) 'Circadian entrainment to the natural light–dark cycle across seasons and the weekend', *Current Biology*, February, 508–13

4 Vitello et al. (2015) 'National Sleep Foundation's sleep quality recommendations', *Sleep Health: Journal of the National Sleep Foundation*, February, 6–19

5 Ruby, P. et al. (2014) 'Resting brain activity varies with dream recall frequency between subjects', *Neuropsychopharmacology*, June, 1594–1602

6 Tomporowski, P.D. (2003) 'Effects of acute bouts of exercise on cognition', *Acta Psycholgica*, March, 297–324

7 Dauwan et al. (2016) 'Exercise improves clinical symptoms, quality of life, global functioning, and depression in schizophrenia: a systematic review and meta-analysis', *Schizophrenia Bulletin*, May, 588–99

8 Ten Brinke, L.S. et al. (2015) 'Aerobic exercise increases hippocampal volume in older women with probable mild cognitive impairment: a 6-month randomised controlled trial', *British Journal of Sports Medicine*, February, 248–54

9 Molteni, R. et al. (2004) 'Voluntary exercise increases axonal regeneration from sensory neurons', *Proceedings of the National Academy of Sciences*, June, 8473–78

10 McGinnis, S. (2016) 'Regular exercise changes the brain to improve memory, thinking skills', *Harvard Health Letter*, 29 November [health.harvard.edu]

11 Bjørnebekk, A. et al. (2005) 'The antidepressant effect of running is associated with increased hippocampal cell proliferation, *International Journal of Neuropsychopharmacology*, September, 357–68

12 Craft, L.L. & F.M. Perna (2004) 'The benefits of exercise for the clinically depressed', *Journal of Clinical Psychiatry*, June, 104–11

13 Hadzi-Pavlovic et al. (2006) 'Omega-3 fatty acids and mood disorders', *The American Journal of Psychiatry*, June, 969–78

14 Marquié, T. et al. (2015) 'Chronic effects of shift work on cognition: findings from the VISAT longitudinal study', *Journal of Occupational and Environmental Medicine*, March, 258–64

15 Whitehurst, L.N. (2015) 'Autonomic activity during sleep predicts memory consolidation in humans', *Proceedings for the National Academy of Sciences*, June, 7272–77

16 Kallistratos, M. (2015) 'Midday naps associated with reduced blood pressure and fewer medications', presented at the European Society of Cardiology, 29 August

17 Rosenberg, J. et al. (2014) '"Early to bed, early to rise": diffusion tensor imaging identifies chronotype-specificity', *NeuroImage*, January, 428–34

18 Giampietro, M. & G.M. Cavallera (2007) 'Morning and evening types and creative thinking', *Science Direct Personality and Individual Differences*, February, 453–63

19 Roberts, R.D. & P.C. Kyllonan (1999) 'Morningness–eveningness and intelligence: early to bed, early to rise will likely make you anything but wise', *Personality and Individual Differences*, December, 1123–33

20 Colberg, S.R. et al. (2010) 'Exercise and type 2 diabetes: American College of Sports Medicine and the American Diabetes Association: joint position statement. Exercise and type-2 diabetes', *Medicine and Science in Sports and Exercise*, December, 2282–303

21 Katzmarzyk P.T. et al. (2009) 'Sitting time and mortality from all causes, cardiovascular disease, and cancer', *Medicine and Science in Sports and Exercise*, May, 998–1005

22 Brown, W.J. et al. (2005) 'Identifying the energy gap: magnitude and determinants of 5-year weight gain in middle age women', *Obesity Research*, August, 1431–41

23 DeBoer, M. (2015) 'Children who watch just one hour of television a day are 50 to 60% more likely to be overweight and 58 to 73% more likely to be obese, compared to children who watch less than an hour', *Pediatric Academic Societies annual meeting*, San Diego, April

24 Levine, J.A. et al. (2006) 'Non-exercise activity thermogenesis: the crouching tiger hidden dragon of societal weight gain', *Arteriosclerosis, Thrombosis, and Vascular Biology*, April, 729–36

25 Labonté-LeMoyne, E. et al. (2015) 'The delayed effect of treadmill desk usage on recall and attention', *Computers in Human Behavior*, May, 1–5

26 Epstein, D.H. & Y. Shaham (2010) 'Cheesecake-eating rats and the question of food addiction', *Nature Neuroscience*, May, 529–31

27 Khan, N.A. et al. (2015) 'Central adiposity is negatively associated with hippocampal-dependent relational memory among overweight and obese children', *The Journal of Pediatrics*, February, 302–08

28 Beilharz, J.E. et al. (2015) 'Diet-induced cognitive deficits: the role of fat and sugar, potential mechanisms and nutritional interventions', *Nutrients*, August, 6719–38

29 Davidson, T.L. et al. (2014) 'An application of Pavlovian principles to the problems of obesity and cognitive decline', *Neurobiology of Learning and Memory*, February, 172–84

30 Holzman, D.C. (2015) 'Evening use of light-emitting eReaders negatively affects sleep, circadian timing, and next-morning alertness', *Proceedings for National American Studies*, January, 1232–37

31 AlDabal, L., & A.S. BaHammam (2011) 'Metabolic, endocrine, and immune consequences of sleep deprivation', *The Open Respiratory Medicine Journal*, June, 31–43

'Joy does not simply happen to us. We have to choose joy and keep choosing it every day.'

Henri Nouwen

Priest, professor, writer and theologian (1932–96)

AND FINALLY . . .

The intention of this book is to provide an overview of just some of the work in neuroscience that has been carried out to date. I hope that it will spark an interest in how your brain works in order to help you get the best out of it, and others around you, during your lifetime.

A great deal of emphasis has been placed on the importance of exercise in boosting memory and wellbeing. Our brain needs us to stay physically as well as cognitively active. We also need to work hard at keeping our brain open: open to other people, open to learning, open to new ideas. Conscious and concerted effort will help us reduce the natural dominance of our negativity bias. And changing just a few habits may make a huge difference to how we feel and behave with the people around us.

We are all, to a greater or lesser extent, authors of our own life's story. We continually make choices about how we live and act – what we eat, how we behave, where we spend our energy and whom we select to be part of our social network. We have the ability to make other people feel important and significant, and every day we choose how to respond to whatever challenges life throws at us.

These choices contribute to the world that we construct around us.

Our brain is a wonderful, changing, mysterious instrument that needs constant care and attention. The thoughts we have, the words we speak and the decisions we make all have an effect on our neural architecture.

We need to respect our brain's power as well as its limitations, and nurture it with healthy habits, good food, regular exercise, supportive and positive friends and, above all, with genuine laughter and joy.

As Dr David Eagleman says:

'The human brain is the most wondrous thing we have discovered in the universe. And it's us.'

NOTE FROM LANSONS

By Suzanne Ellis, Director

At Lansons we know the value of effective communication. We advise companies on leadership engagement, organisation change, reputation management, public affairs and strategic communications.

Our aim is to engage people on a deep level. That is why we believe in this book. We all need to recognise that our brain is at the centre of all of our communication, and through our collaboration with Dr Helena Boschi we can add another dimension to the work we offer.

The combination of science, practical experience, ideas and new techniques will be, we hope, valuable for everyone we work with.

We hope you enjoy learning more about the science behind *Why We Do What We Do.*

INDEX